level

C

Rehearsing
for the Common
Core Standards
Mathematics

RALLY!
EDUCATION

We're all about student success!

ISBN 978-1-4204-7864-8
R 7864-8

0813.MAQ

RALLY! EDUCATION • 22 Railroad Avenue, Glen Head, NY 11545 • (888) 99-RALLY

Contents

Introduction 4
Math Reference Sheet 5

Chapter 1: Operations & Algebraic Thinking . . .7

Cluster: Represent and solve problems involving multiplication and division.
Lesson 1: 3.OA.1, 3.OA.3 8
Lesson 2: 3.OA.1, 3.OA.3 12
Lesson 3: 3.OA.2, 3.OA.3 16
Lesson 4: 3.OA.2, 3.OA.3 20
Lesson 5: 3.OA.3, 3.OA.2, 3.OA.7, 3.OA.8 24
Lesson 6: 3.OA.3, 3.OA.2, 3.OA.8 28
Lesson 7: 3.OA.4, 3.OA.1, 3.OA.2, 3.OA.3 32
Lesson 8: 3.OA.4, 3.OA.2, 3.OA.3 36

Cluster: Understand properties of multiplication and the relationship between multiplication and division.
Lesson 9: 3.OA.5, 3.OA.7 40
Lesson 10: 3.OA.5, 3.OA.7 44
Lesson 11: 3.OA.6, 3.OA.7, 3.NF.1 49

Cluster: Multiply and divide within 100.
Lesson 12: 3.OA.7, 3.OA.3, 3.OA.6 52
Lesson 13: 3.OA.7, 3.OA.3, 3.OA.6 55

Cluster: Solve Problems involving the four operations, and identify and explain patters in arithmetic.
Lesson 14: 3.OA.8, 3.OA.3 58
Lesson 15: 3.OA.8, 3.OA.3, 3.NBT.3 61
Lesson 16: 3.OA.9, 3.OA.5 64

Chapter 2: Number & Operations in Base Ten . . .69

Cluster: Use place value understanding and properties of operations to perform multi-digit arithmetic.
Lesson 17: 3.NBT.1, 3.OA.8, 3.NBT.3 70
Lesson 18: 3.NBT.2, 3.OA.8, 3.NBT.1 74
Lesson 19: 3.NBT.2, 3.OA.8, 3.NBT.1 78
Lesson 20: 3.NBT.3, 3.OA.3, 3.OA.8, 3.NBT.2 82

Chapter 3: Number & Operations—Fractions . . .87

Cluster: Develop understanding of fractions as numbers.
Lesson 21: 3.NF.1, 3.OA.3 88
Lesson 22: 3.NF.1, 3.OA.3 92
Lesson 23: 3.NF.2a, 3.OA.1, 3.NF.3d 98
Lesson 24: 3.NF.2b, 3.G.2 103
Lesson 25: 3.NF.3a, 3.NF.3b, 3.G.2 108
Lesson 26: 3.NF.3c, 3 NF.3a, 3 NF.2a, 3.OA.7 112
Lesson 27: 3.NF.3d, 3.G.2 118

Chapter 4: Measurement & Data 123

Cluster: Solve problems involving measurement and estimation of intervals of time, liquid volumes, and masses of objects.
Lesson 28: 3.MD.1, 3.OA.8 124
Lesson 29: 3.MD.1, 3.NBT.2 .128
Lesson 30: 3.MD.2, 3.OA.3 132
Lesson 31: 3.MD.2, 3.OA.3 136

Cluster: Represent and interpret data.
Lesson 32: 3.MD.3, 3.OA.3 140
Lesson 33: 3.MD.3, 3.OA.3 144
Lesson 34: 3.MD.4, 3.NF.2 148
Lesson 35: 3.MD.4, 3.NF.2 154

Cluster: Geometric Measurement: understand concepts of area and relate area to multiplication and to addition.
Lesson 36: 3.MD.5a, 3.MD.5b, 3.G.2 158
Lesson 37: 3.MD.6, 3.G.2 162
Lesson 38: 3.MD.7a, 3.OA.3, 3.G.2 168
Lesson 39: 3.MD.7b, 3.OA.3, 3.NBT.3 173
Lesson 40: 3.MD.7c, 3.OA.3, 3.NBT.3 176
Lesson 41: 3.MD.7d, 3.OA.3, 3.NBT.3 181
Lesson 42: 3.MD.7d, 3.OA.3, 3.NBT.3 186

Cluster: Geometric Measurement: recognize perimeter as an attribute of plane figures and distinguish between linear and area measurements.
Lesson 43: 3.MD.8, 3.OA.3, 3.OA.4 190
Lesson 44: 3.MD.8, 3.OA.3 194
Lesson 45: 3.MD.8, 3.OA.3 198

Chapter 5: Geometry 203

Cluster: Reason with shapes and their attributes.
Lesson 46: 3.G.1 204
Lesson 47: 3.G.1 209
Lesson 48: 3.G.2, 3.NF.1, 3.MD.6 213
Lesson 49: 3.G.2, 3.NF.1 217

Chapter 6: Review 223
Lesson 50 224
Lesson 51 228
Lesson 52 232
Lesson 53 235
Lesson 54 238
Lesson 55 242
Lesson 56 247

Introduction

About this book

Rehearsing for the Common Core State Standards in Math provides students with practice at solving multi-step math problems that are aligned to the Common Core State Standards. This book includes six chapters. The first five chapters are arranged by math domain. The last chapter is a review of all five math domains.

The domains that are covered in this book include—

- Operations and Algebraic Thinking
- Number and Operations in Base Ten
- Number and Operations—Fractions
- Measurement and Data
- Geometry

Chapters 1–5 include several different lessons that are grouped by math cluster. Many of the lessons include *Background Information* that is followed by a series of questions. In some instances, the Background Information includes data, graphs, charts, or pictures that students will need to use when answering the questions that follow. There are times when students will need to turn back to the page with this information in order to answer a question.

Each lesson in Chapters 1 through 5 lists the standards that are covered by the problems in the lesson. The standards for each lesson are identified as *primary* or *secondary* standards. On some occasions, there are included *review* standards.

- The *primary* standard is the focus of the lesson.
- The *secondary* standards are those standards that are also connected to the lesson but not its main emphasis.
- The *review* standards are standards from an earlier grade that students need to be competent in to solve the problems.

In Chapter 6, there are separate review lessons. These review lessons include math problems from all of the domains that students have practiced throughout the book. Chapter 6 can be used to determine how well students are able to answer different types of math problems. All of the math problems in this book have been developed to help students improve their math skills and become better problem solvers in math.

Math Reference Sheet

To solve some math problems you may need to use the formulas and measurement conversions on these two pages.

Formulas

Area

Rectangle: $A = \text{Length} \times \text{Width}$

Square: $A = \text{Side} \times \text{Side}$

Perimeter

Rectangle: $P = (2 \times \text{Length}) + (2 \times \text{Width})$

Square: $P = 4 \times \text{Side}$

Measurement Conversions

Length

Metric

1 meter = 100 centimeters

1 centimeter = 10 millimeters

Customary

1 yard = 3 feet

1 foot = 12 inches

Capacity and Volume

Metric

1 liter = 1,000 milliliters

Customary

1 gallon = 4 quarts

1 quart = 2 pints

1 pint = 2 cups

Mass and Weight

Metric

1 kilogram = 1,000 grams

1 gram = 1,000 milligrams

Customary

1 ton = 2,000 pounds

1 pound = 16 ounces

Time

1 year = 365 days

1 year = 12 months

1 year = 52 weeks

1 week = 7 days

1 day = 24 hours

1 hour = 60 minutes

1 minute = 60 seconds

Chapter 1

Operations and Algebraic Thinking

Chapter 1 focuses on the domain Operations and Algebraic Thinking. The chapter contains lessons. Each lesson covers a cluster and several of the Math Standards in that cluster. For some clusters, there are more than one lesson. The clusters covered in this chapter are listed below.

Clusters:

• Represent and solve problems involving multiplication and division.

• Understand properties of multiplication and the relationship between multiplication and division.

• Multiply and divide within 100.

• Solve problems involving the four operations, and identify and explain patterns in arithmetic.

Lesson 1

Domain: Operations and Algebraic Thinking
Cluster: Represent and solve problems involving multiplication and division.
Standards: Primary 3.OA.1; Secondary 3.OA.3; Review 2.MD.10

Background Information:

Main Street Veterinary Clinic examines and treats pets. It also sells pet products. Its employees use multiplication to keep track of the number of pets they examine and the number of products they sell.

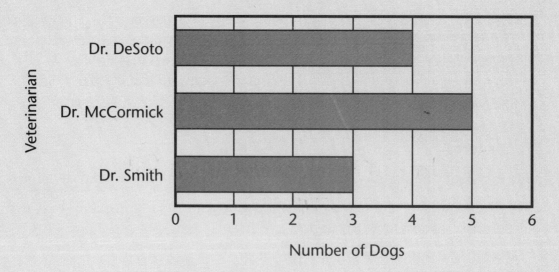

1 The bar graph shows the number of dogs that were examined by each veterinarian at Main Street Veterinary Clinic on Monday. Think about what information you can find by looking at the bar graph.

Part A   Dr. McCormick wants to record the total number of paws she examined on Monday. How many paws does each dog have? How many dogs did Dr. McCormick examine? Draw a model to show the number of dogs and the number of paws that each dog has.

There are 5 dogs and each dog has 4 paws.

Part B   Explain how you can use the model you drew in Part A to find the number of paws Dr. McCormick examined in all. How many paws did Dr. McCormick examine in all on Monday?

I can use the information I know and multiply it.
4 × 5 = 20
Dr. McCormick examined 20 paws on Monday.

2 Main Street Veterinary Clinic wants to record the total number of paws examined by all the veterinarians on Monday. How many dogs were examined by each doctor? How many dogs were examined in all?

Dr. DeSoto ~ 4 dogs
Dr. McCormick ~ 5 dogs
Dr. Smith ~ 3 dogs

4 + 5 + 3 = 12 dogs total

3 Describe how you could show the total number of paws examined in all with a model showing equal groups. Write a multiplication sentence to show the total number of paws examined by all the veterinarians. How many paws did the veterinarians examine in all on Monday?

12 × 4 = 48

48 paws were examined on Monday.

4 Main Street Veterinary Clinic received 3 boxes of vitamins in the mail. There are 5 bottles of vitamins in each box of vitamins. An employee needs to record the total number of bottles of vitamins that the clinic received.

Part A   How many boxes of vitamins were received? How many bottles of vitamins are in each box? Draw equal groups to show how many boxes of vitamins were received and how many bottles are in each box.

Part B   Explain how you can use the model you drew in Part A to find the number of bottles of vitamins received. How many bottles of vitamins did the clinic receive in all?

You can do 3 × 15 = 15
The clinic received 15 bottles
of vitamins.

Part C   The mail carrier just delivered another box of vitamins that had fallen in the mail truck. Find the total number of bottles of vitamins that the clinic received, including this last box of vitamins. Show your work.

4 × 5 = 20 bottles of vitamins

or

15 + 5 = 20

Lesson 2

Domain: Operations and Algebraic Thinking
Cluster: Represent and solve problems involving multiplication and division.
Standards: Primary 3.OA.1; Secondary 3.OA.3

Background Information:

Mrs. Rodegra's class is planning a Valentine's Day party. There are 24 students in the class. They can use multiplication to figure out how many items they will need for the party.

The class will need plates, napkins, and forks for the party. The table shows how many of each come in a package.

Item	Number in a Package
Plates	6
Napkins	12
Forks	8

1 Mandie is a student in Mrs. Rodegra's class. Mandie's mother will bake 4 apple pies for the party. She needs 3 apples for each pie.

Part A   Draw equal groups to show the number of pies and the number of apples in each pie.

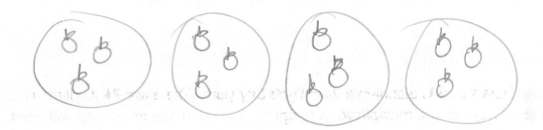

Part B   Look at the model you made in Part A. Use the model to write an addition sentence and a multiplication sentence that show the number of apples Mandie's mother will need to make 4 pies. How many apples will she need to make 4 pies?

$3 + 3 + 3 + 3 = 12$

$3 \times 4 = 12$

she will need 12 apples to make 4 apple pies,

2 Tyler drew this model to show how the 24 students in Mrs. Rodegra's class can be placed into equal groups. Is his model correct? Explain why or why not.

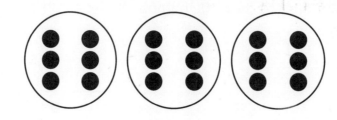

His model is incorrect because there are only 18 students shown in the model not 24.

3 Kyle's mother bought 3 packages of plates. Are there enough plates for all 24 students? If not, how many more plates are needed? Show your work.

$3 \times 6 = 18$

No there are not because 3 packages of plates is only good for 18 students. Kyle's mother needs one more package of plates.

4 Maria's mother will bring napkins and forks. How many packages of each does she need to buy for all 24 students? Show your work.

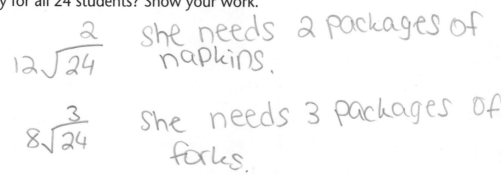

$12\overline{)24}$ gives 2 — she needs 2 packages of napkins.

$8\overline{)24}$ gives 3 — she needs 3 packages of forks.

5 There are 4 tables in Mrs. Rodegra's classroom that will be used for the party.

Part A   Draw a model to show how the 24 students can be placed into equal groups at the 4 tables.

Part B   Use the model you drew in Part A to write an addition sentence and a multiplication sentence that show the number of students at each table. How many students will sit at each table?

$$6 + 6 + 6 + 6 = 24$$

$$6 \times 4 = 24$$

6 students will sit at each table.

Lesson 3

Domain: Operations and Algebraic Thinking
Cluster: Represent and solve problems involving multiplication and division.
Standards: Primary 3.OA.2; Secondary 3.OA.3

Background Information:

Many people have collections of favorite objects. They may divide their objects into groups with an equal number of objects in each group.

Three siblings collect old postcards. The table shows how many postcards each sibling has collected.

Name	Number of Postcards
Sophia	35
Jake	25
Zoe	15

1 Christopher has a collection of 15 rocks he gathered while on vacation.

Part A   Christopher puts an equal number of rocks in 5 boxes. Complete the
model to show and write how many rocks he placed in each box.

Part B   Describe another way Christopher could arrange 15 rocks to make
equal groups.

He could use 3 boxs and
put 5 rocks in each box.

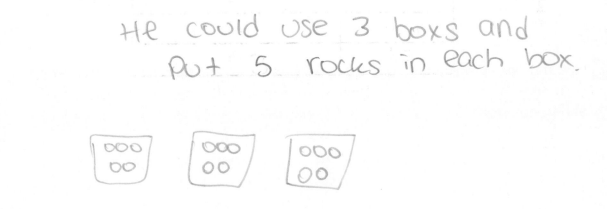

17

2 Ella has 20 snow globes that she wants to display in equal groups.
Show 2 different ways Ella can make equal groups of snow globes.

3 Sophia puts her postcards in an album. She puts an equal number of postcards on
7 pages in her album. How many postcards does she put on each page? Show
your work.

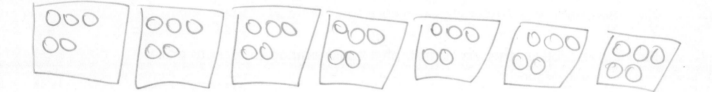

4 Jake and Zoe combine their postcards. They put an equal number of postcards on
each page of an 8-page album. How many postcards do they put on each page?
Show your work.

5 Justin has won 16 trophies playing baseball. His mother bought a display case for him to keep the trophies in. The case has 4 shelves. Justin wants to put an equal number of trophies on each shelf. How many trophies should he put on each shelf? Show your work.

6 Serena has a collection of 18 dolls that she no longer wants. She will give them to her 3 younger cousins. She wants to give the same number of dolls to each cousin. How many dolls will Serena give to each cousin? Show your work.

She will give 6 dolls to each cousin.

Lesson 4

Domain: Operations and Algebraic Thinking
Cluster: Represent and solve problems involving multiplication and division.
Standards: Primary 3.OA.2; Secondary 3.OA.3

Background Information:

Classrooms have many supplies that will be divided evenly among students in the classroom.

This table shows the number of drawing supplies in each classroom.

Type	Number
Colored Pencils	15
Markers	24
Crayons	30
Drawing Paper	45

This table shows the number of craft supplies in each classroom.

Type	Number
Buttons	18
Pieces of Ribbon	28
Craft Sticks	36
Stickers	48

1 The colored pencils are being shared equally among 3 students in the blue group. The markers are being shared equally among 4 students in the red group. Which group has more drawing tools for each student? How many more? Draw a model to help you answer these questions.

2 There are 15 students working in the writing center. Can each student get 3 crayons? If not, how many crayons can each student get? Draw a model to help you answer these questions.

3 The markers are being shared equally among 4 students in the green group. The crayons are being shared equally among 5 students in the yellow group. Compare the number of drawing tools that each student gets in the two groups by drawing a model.

4 There are 6 students at the craft table. Which craft supplies can be shared equally among the 6 students? Draw a model to help you answer this question.

5 Now there are 4 students at the craft table. Which craft supplies can be shared equally among the 4 students? Draw a model to help you answer this question.

6 The teacher divided the craft sticks equally among some students. Each student got 9 craft sticks. The teacher also divided the buttons equally among some other students. Each student got 9 buttons. How many students got craft sticks? How many students got buttons? Draw a model to help you answer these questions.

7 The class is reviewing math facts. There are 35 addition flash cards and 32 subtraction flash cards. A group of 5 students equally share the addition flash cards. A group of 4 students equally share the subtraction flash cards. Which group has more flash cards per student? Draw a model to help you answer these questions.

Lesson 5

Domain: Operations and Algebraic Thinking
Cluster: Represent and solve problems involving multiplication and division.
Standards: Primary 3.OA.3; Secondary 3.OA.2, 3.OA.7, 3.OA.8; Review 2.OA.1, 2.MD.10

Background Information:

Mrs. Demko's third-grade class is learning about animals. The students are reading nonfiction books to learn facts about animals. Sometimes it is helpful to use multiplication or division to better understand facts that relate to a group.

Each day, Mrs. Demko asked students to share facts about an animal they are studying. The bar graph shows the total number of facts that 4 of the students shared in 5 days.

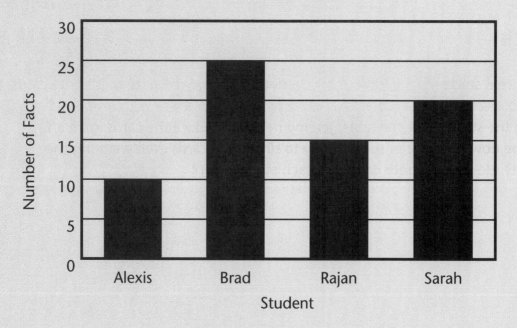

1 Brad shared an equal number of animal facts each day for 5 days. Sarah also shared an equal number of animal facts each day for 5 days. How many facts did these two students share in all each day? Show your work.

2 Alexis shared an equal number of animal facts each day for 5 days. Rajan also shared an equal number of animal facts each day for 5 days. How many more facts did Rajan share each day than Alexis? Show your work.

3 There are 6 students at a table. Mrs. Demko hands them a stack of 30 note cards. Each note card has an animal fact. She asks Jeremy to divide the cards equally among the students at the table. Jeremy decides to place the cards in an array. Describe how Jeremy can use an array to divide the cards evenly among the students. How many note cards will each student get?

The table shows the mass of four types of hummingbirds.

Type	Mass (in grams)
Anna's	6
Black-chinned	4
Broad-tailed	3
Costa's	2

4 There are 3 black-chinned hummingbirds and 2 of another type of hummingbird in a yard. The birds have a total mass of 18 grams. What other type of hummingbird is in the yard? Explain.

5 A bird rescue center has 4 Costa's hummingbirds and 3 of another type of hummingbird. The birds have a total mass of 20 grams. What other type of hummingbird is at the bird rescue center? Explain.

The table shows the length of three types of snakes.

Snake Type	Length (in inches)
Smooth Earth Snake	7
Southeastern Crowned Snake	8
Northern Brown Snake	9

6 On a nature walk, Jessie saw 4 smooth earth snakes and 2 northern brown snakes. What is the total length of all the snakes she saw? Show your work.

7 A reptile center has 3 of one type of snake. The combined length of the 3 snakes is 24 inches. The reptile center also has 4 of another type of snake. The combined length of the 4 snakes is 28 inches. What two types of snakes does the reptile center have? Explain.

Lesson 6

Domain: Operations and Algebraic Thinking
Cluster: Represent and solve problems involving multiplication and division.
Standards: Primary 3.OA.3; Secondary 3.OA.2, 3.OA.8; Review 2.OA.1

Background Information:

Mr. Reynolds owns a garden center. Both he and his customers often use multiplication or division to solve problems related to gardening.

Mr. Reynolds sells trays of seedlings. The table shows the number of seedlings in each tray for four types of flowers.

Flower Type	Number in Each Tray
Carnation	6
Daisy	8
Rose	4
Gladiolus	3

1 Jessica bought 2 trays of carnations and 3 trays of roses. How many seedlings did she buy in all? Show your work.

2 Brandon bought 3 trays of daisies and 3 trays of gladiolus. How many more daisies than gladiolus did he buy? Show your work.

3 Heather wants to plant 20 seedlings of one type of flower in her garden. Which type of seedling can she buy so that she uses all the seedlings in the trays without having any left over? How many trays should she buy? Show your work.

4 Will bought 18 trees from Mr. Reynolds. He wants to plant the trees in a field. On the grid below, draw two arrays to show different ways Will can plant the trees in equal rows.

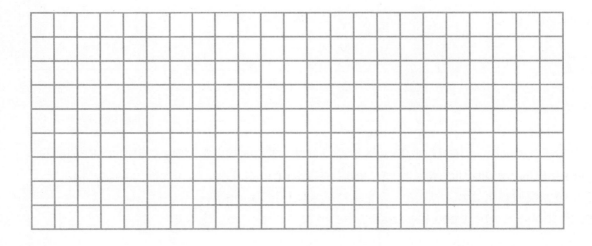

5 Mr. Reynolds had 32 bags of mulch for sale. Four customers came in and bought an equal number of bags of mulch. Mr. Reynolds had only 4 bags of mulch left. How many bags of mulch did each customer buy? Show your work.

6 Mr. Reynolds received a shipment of 40 bags of planting soil. He sold 8 bags. He divided the rest of the bags into 4 equal stacks. How many bags of planting soil did Mr. Reynolds put in each stack? Show your work.

7 Tanner bought 18 sections of curved fence from Mr. Reynolds. He plans to put 3 sections of fence around each tree in his yard. If Tanner has 8 trees, how many more sections of curved fence does he need? Show your work.

Lesson 7

Domain: Operations and Algebraic Thinking
Cluster: Represent and solve problems involving multiplication and division.
Standards: Primary 3.OA.4; Secondary 3.OA.1, 3.OA.2, 3.OA.3

Background Information:

The third grade classes at Southside Elementary School are practicing finding the unknown number in multiplication and division problems. The students learn that they can use multiplication and division in real-world situations as well as in problems presented in the classroom.

1 Keisha plans to write 24 thank-you notes for birthday presents she received. Thank-you notes come in packs of 8. Keisha writes this equation to find the number of packs of thank-you notes she needs to buy.

$$n \times 8 = 24$$

Show how Keisha can use an array to find the unknown factor. How many packs of thank-you notes does Keisha need to buy?

2 Mrs. Greene wrote these 2 equations on the board and asked students to tell which has a greater product.

$$5 \times 8 = \square \qquad 4 \times 9 = \square$$

Gregory says the first equation has a greater product. Alisha says the second equation has a greater product. Find the missing product in each equation. What strategy did you use to find the missing products? Do you agree with Gregory or Alisha? Explain.

3 Mr. Schwartz wrote this equation on the board.

$$27 \div x = 9$$

Which strategy can you use to find the unknown number? Explain. What is the unknown number?

4 Jessica came across this problem in her homework.

$$6 \times \triangle = 60$$

Explain how Jessica can find the unknown number. What is the unknown number?

5 Mrs. Nelson is setting up 28 chairs in rows for a meeting. She places an equal number of chairs in 4 rows. How many chairs did Mrs. Nelson put in each row? This equation represents the situation.

$$28 \div c = 4$$

Which strategy can you use to find the unknown number? Explain how you would use this strategy. What is the unknown number? What does this number represent?

6 Mr. Jenkins wrote this equation on the board. He told the class that the expression on the right side of the equals sign must have the same value as the expression on the left side of the equals sign.

$$8 \times 8 = 60 \ \square \ 4$$

Find the missing operation symbol that makes the equation true. Explain how you got your answer.

7 The next day, Mr. Jenkins wrote this equation on the board.

$$45 \div 9 = 35 \ \square \ 7$$

Find the missing operation symbol that makes the equation true. Explain how you got your answer.

Lesson 8

Domain: Operations and Algebraic Thinking
Cluster: Represent and solve problems involving multiplication and division.
Standards: Primary 3.OA.4; Secondary 3.OA.2, 3.OA.3

Background Information:

The third grade classes are using real-world situations and classroom work to practice analyzing multiplication and division equations. Their goal is to find the unknown number in these multiplication and division problems.

1 Nick is filling baskets with fruit. It takes him 1 minute to fill 3 baskets. How long will it take Nick to fill 30 baskets? Write a division equation to represent the situation. Use a letter to represent the unknown number. Then solve your equation. Describe the strategy you use to solve the equation.

2 Mrs. Katz wrote this equation on the board.

$$5 = \boxed{} \div 3$$

Denise says the missing number is 2. Derek says the missing number is 15. Find the missing number in the equation. Who do you agree with, Denise or Derek? Explain the strategy you used to find the missing number.

3 Maria came across this problem in her homework.

$$24 \div x = 6$$

This number line appears below the problem.

Maria is not sure how to use the number line to solve the problem. Describe the steps that Maria should follow to solve the problem using the number line. What is the missing number?

4 Hania's class is going to the science center. The 28 students from the class are divided into 7 equal groups. How many students are in each group? The following equation represents the situation.

$$28 \div 7 = s$$

Describe a strategy you can use to find the unknown number. What is the unknown number? What does the unknown number represent?

5 Mrs. Johnson wrote this equation on the board.

$$36 = \triangle \times 6$$

Michael needs to solve the equation. Describe and model a strategy that Michael can use to find the unknown factor. What is the unknown factor?

6 Mr. Newman wrote these two equations on the board. He asked which product has a lesser value.

$$3 \times 8 = \square \qquad 4 \times 7 = \square$$

Jackson says the first product has a lesser value. Ren says the second product has a lesser value. Find the missing product in each equation. Describe the strategy you used to find the missing products. Who is correct, Jackson or Ren? Explain how you know.

7 Mrs. Allred wrote this equation on the board. She asked students to write an operation symbol in the box so that the expression on the right side of the equation is equal to the expression on the left side of the equation.

$$4 \times 9 = 40 \; \square \; 4$$

Find the missing operation symbol that makes the equation true. Describe how you made the equation true. What is the missing operation symbol?

Lesson 9

Domain: Operations and Algebraic Thinking
Cluster: Understand properties of multiplication and the relationship between multiplication and division.
Standards: Primary 3.OA.5; Secondary 3.OA.7

Background Information:

Mrs. Griffin's class is learning about the properties of multiplication. They will use objects in the classroom to practice applying the properties to solve multiplication problems.

1 Mrs. Griffin draws 2 circles on the board and places 4 magnets in each circle to form a model like the one shown.

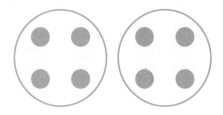

Write a multiplication sentence for the model. Then use the Commutative Property of Multiplication to write a related multiplication sentence.

2 The class is practicing using the Distributive Property to solve multiplication problems. Mrs. Griffin writes this problem on the board.

$$6 \times 7 = \underline{\quad}$$

Part A   In the space below, draw an array to show 6×7.

Part B   Draw a line to break the array you drew into two smaller arrays for multiplication facts you know. Write the facts shown by the two smaller arrays. Then use these facts to find the product of the whole array. Show your work.

3 Mrs. Griffin writes this problem on the board.

$$8 \times 5 = \underline{\qquad}$$

Show how you can use the Distributive Property by using addends for one of the factors. Find the product.

4 The class is practicing using the Associative Property of Multiplication. Mrs. Griffin writes this problem on the board.

$$4 \times (2 \times 2) = \underline{\qquad}$$

Use the Associative Property of Multiplication to change the grouping with parentheses. Then find the product.

5 The class is given the following problem.

$$7 \times 4 = \underline{\quad}$$

Marina says she will use the Distributive Property to solve the problem. Charlie says he will use the Associative Property to solve the problem. Whose strategy do you think will work? Explain how you know. Show how to use the strategy to find the product.

6 Mrs. Griffin writes the following problem.

$$8 \times 3 = \underline{\quad}$$

Zoe is not sure which multiplication property to use to solve the problem. Which strategy would you recommend? Explain why. Show how to use the strategy to find the product.

Lesson 10

Domain: Operations and Algebraic Thinking
Cluster: Understand properties of multiplication and the relationship between multiplication and division.
Standards: Primary 3.OA.5; Secondary 3.OA.7

Background Information:

Chester is helping out on his uncle's farm over the summer. He decides to practice using the multiplication properties he has learned to find how many animals he sees around the farm.

1 Chester goes into the henhouse. He sees 2 shelves with 3 hens on each shelf on one wall. He sees 3 shelves with 2 hens on each shelf on another wall.

For each wall, write a multiplication sentence that can be used to show the number of hens on the wall. Find the product for each sentence. What multiplication property is modeled by the two multiplication sentences? Explain. How many hens are in the henhouse in all?

2 Chester's uncle asks him to feed the pigs. There are 3 pens with 8 pigs in each pen. Chester decides to use the Distributive Property to find how many pigs there are in all. Write a multiplication sentence to represent the number of pens and the number of pigs in each pen. Then show how to use the Distributive Property to find the product. How many pigs are there in all?

3 Chester walks out in the pasture and sees 3 groups of horses. There are 2 pairs of horses in each group. Chester writes this multiplication sentence to represent the number of horses.

$$3 \times (2 \times 2) = \underline{\quad\quad}$$

Use the Associative Property of Multiplication to show another way Chester could group the factors. Then find the product. Show your work. How many horses did Chester see in all?

4 There are 4 ponds on the farm. Chester counts 6 ducks in each pond. Chester writes the multiplication sentence 4 × 6 = _____ to show the number of ducks in the ponds.

Use the Commutative Property to write a related multiplication sentence to show the number of ducks in the ponds. Find the product. How many ducks are there altogether in the ponds on the farm?

5 Chester went to collect eggs from the henhouse. Nine hens had laid eggs. Each hen laid 3 eggs. Chester writes this multiplication sentence to represent the number of eggs he collected.

$$9 \times 3 = \underline{\quad}$$

Name a multiplication property Chester can use to find the product. Model how to use the property to find the product. How many eggs did Chester collect in all?

6 Chester raked leaves in front of the farmhouse and made 4 rows of leaves with 3 piles in each row. He also made 4 rows with 3 piles of leaves in the back of the house. The following multiplication sentence represents all the piles of leaves Chester raked.

$$(4 \times 3) \times 2 = \underline{\hspace{1cm}}$$

Use the Associative Property of Multiplication to show another way Chester could group the factors. Then use one of the multiplication sentences to find the product. Show your work. How many piles of leaves did Chester rake in all?

7 Chester helped his uncle check on the cows. The cows were grouped equally in 4 fields. There were 9 cows in each field.

Write a multiplication sentence you can use to represent the fields and the number of cows in each field. Use the Distributive Property to find the total number of cows. Show your work. How many cows in all did Chester and his uncle check on?

Lesson 11

Domain: Operations and Algebraic Thinking
Cluster: Understand properties of multiplication and the relationship between multiplication and division.
Standards: Primary 3.OA.6; Secondary 3.OA.7, 3.NF.1

Background Information:

Bree's Bakery makes and sells many kinds of breads and pastries. Bree and her customers often use multiplication and division to figure out how many.

The table shows some of the items available today in Bree's Bakery.

Item	Number for Sale
Oatmeal cookies	45
Cheese Danish	24
Croissants	36
Fruit tarts	30
Red velvet cake slices	18

1 Bree baked all the oatmeal cookies and the all fruit tarts at the same time. She put 9 oatmeal cookies on a tray and 5 fruit tarts on a tray. How many trays did Bree use in all to bake the cookies and the fruit tarts? Show your work.

2 Mrs. Blakely purchased 6 oatmeal cookies for $12 and 3 cheese Danishes for $9. What was the price for each cookie and each cheese Danish? Show your work.

3 Bree displays the croissants by placing 6 croissants on a platter. How many platters does Bree need to display all the croissants? How many fewer platters would she need if she placed 9 croissants on a platter? Show your work.

4 Mr. Reynolds bought 15 fruit tarts and 9 slices of red velvet cake. He divided the pastries equally among his 3 employees. How many pastries in all did each employee get? Show your work.

5 Mr. Lee bought one-fourth of the croissants. He paid $18. What was the price for each croissant? Show your work.

6 Lindsay bought 6 oatmeal cookies and 6 cheese Danishes. She paid $30 in all. If cheese Danishes are $3 each, what is the price of each oatmeal cookie? Show your work.

7 Michael bought an equal number of each kind of pastry. He bought 15 pastries in all. How many of each kind of pastry did Michael buy? Show your work.

Lesson 12

Domain: Operations and Algebraic Thinking
Cluster: Multiply and divide within 100.
Standards: Primary 3.OA.7; Secondary 3.OA.3, 3.OA.6

Background Information:

Mr. Zhang owns a market in town. He often uses multiplication and division to figure out how many items he receives.

The table shows the number of different kinds of drinks for sale in the produce area of Mr. Zhang's market.

Drink	Number
Orange juice	24
Grapefruit juice	20
Fruit smoothies	18

1 Mr. Zhang received a shipment of oranges. He received 2 boxes. Each box contains 4 crates, and each crate contains 8 oranges. How many oranges did Mr. Zhang receive in all? Show your work.

2 Mr. Zhang has 18 boxes of crackers to display. He divides them evenly between 2 shelves. He places 3 rows of boxes on each shelf. How many boxes of crackers are in each row? Show your work.

3 A customer purchases 3 pounds of hamburger meat and 2 pounds of cheese. The hamburger meat costs $3 per pound and the cheese costs $5 per pound. What is the total amount the customer pays for the hamburger meat and cheese? Show your work.

4 Mr. Zhang spends 5 minutes twice a day talking to customers and asking them about their shopping experience. What is the total number of minutes that Mr. Zhang spends talking to customers in 4 days? Show your work.

5 Mr. Zhang has 5 employees who each work 8 hours each day. He has 4 employees who each work 5 hours each day. What is the total number of hours that all his employees work each day? Show your work.

6 Mr. Zhang places all the juices in rows. He places the different types of juices in separate rows. He places 4 orange juice bottles in each row and 5 grapefruit juice bottles in each row. Which drink has more rows of bottles? How many more? Show your work.

7 A customer buys 4 fruit smoothies and 2 bottles of grapefruit juice for $20. Each bottle of grapefruit juice costs $2. What is the cost of each fruit smoothie? Show your work.

Lesson 13

Domain: Operations and Algebraic Thinking
Cluster: Multiply and divide within 100.
Standards: Primary 3.OA.7; Secondary 3.OA.3, 3.OA.6

Background Information:

Mrs. Alvarez owns a hobby store. She often uses multiplication and division to figure out how many of each item she has in the store.

The chart shows the prices for different sizes of kites that Mrs. Alvarez sells in her store.

Kite Size	Price
Small	$4
Medium	$6
Large	$9

1 Mrs. Alvarez sold $52 worth of kites on Monday. She sold 4 small kites and 3 medium kites. How many large kites did she sell on Monday? Show your work.

2   The owner of a summer camp came in and purchased 2 of each size kite. What was the total cost of the kites? Show your work.

3   Mrs. Alvarez received a shipment of 27 kites. There was an equal number of each kite size in the shipment. She placed the kites on 3 shelves. There are an equal number of each size kite on each shelf. How many small kites did Mrs. Alvarez place on each shelf? Show your work.

4   Mrs. Alvarez has 28 blue camera cases and 17 red camera cases in one large bin. She wants to place an equal number of camera cases in 9 smaller bins. How many camera cases will she place in each bin? Show your work.

5 Mrs. Alvarez had 30 model train cars for sale. She sold an equal number of model train cars to 7 customers. At the end of the day there were 9 model train cars left. How many model train cars did each customer buy? Show your work.

6 Mrs. Alvarez sells model car kits and model plane kits. She has 4 rows of 6 model car kits on one shelf. On another shelf, she has 5 rows of 4 model plane kits. How many model car and model plane kits does Mrs. Alvarez have on the shelves in all? Show your work.

7 Mrs. Alvarez received a shipment of 24 large camera lenses and 30 small camera lenses. She places the camera lenses in display cases. She can fit 3 large lenses on each shelf and 5 small lenses on each shelf. How many more shelves will she use to display the large lenses than to display the small lenses? Show your work.

Lesson 14

Domain: Operations and Algebraic Thinking
Cluster: Solve problems involving the four operations, and identify and explain patterns in arithmetic.
Standards: Primary 3.OA.8; Secondary 3.OA.3

Background Information:

Jessica and Sam each have jobs for the summer. Jessica is working in her family's restaurant. Sam is working in a grocery store. They both realize that they can use math to help them with their jobs.

1 The restaurant received 50 clean tablecloths from a laundry service. Jessica placed 1 tablecloth on each of the 10 tables in the restaurant. She divided the remaining tablecloths into 5 equal stacks. How many tablecloths did Jessica put in each stack? Show your work.

2 The grocery store receives 5 full boxes of cans of green beans. Sam takes 8 cans to restock the grocery shelf. There are 42 cans of green beans left. How many cans of green beans were in each box? Show your work.

3 Jessica works at a restaurant and is responsible for keeping track of what is sold throughout the day. She finds that the restaurant sold 5 roast beef sandwiches and 6 Greek salads for a total of $67. The price of a roast beef sandwich is $5. What is the price of a Greek salad? Show your work.

4 Sam counts 5 loaves of bread left on the shelf. The grocery store receives 2 equal boxes of bread loaves. Now there are 21 loaves of bread. How many loaves of bread were in each box? Show your work.

5 Sam has 40 apples to display in the produce section. He forms 4 rows of apples with an equal number of apples in each row. Sam has 4 apples left over. How many apples did Sam place in each row? What is another way that Sam could arrange the apples in rows of equal size so that he uses all 40 apples? Show your work.

6 Jessica has a large, 60-ounce container of ketchup that she is using to fill ketchup bottles. She has 8 bottles to fill. She places the same number of ounces in each bottle. When she finishes, there are 12 ounces of ketchup left in the large container. How many ounces of ketchup did Jessica put in each bottle? Show your work.

7 Jessica waits on a total of 4 tables for breakfast and lunch. She receives a $3 tip from each table during breakfast. She receives a $4 tip from each table during lunch. What is the total amount in tips that Jessica received? Show your work.

Lesson 15

Domain: Operations and Algebraic Thinking
Cluster: Solve problems involving the four operations, and identify and explain
patterns in arithmetic.
Standards: Primary 3.OA.8; Secondary 3.OA.3, 3.NBT.3

Background Information:

Mrs. Nowak's class wants to go on a field trip to the science museum. The cost of the trip is $250. The class earns money by having a bake sale each week for 6 weeks. The class earns $20 each week at the bake sale.

1   **Part A**   Write an equation to represent the situation described above. Use a letter to represent the amount of money the class still needs to earn. How much more money does Mrs. Nowak's class still need to earn to pay for the field trip? Show your work.

Part B   A parent donates $50 to help cover the cost of the field trip. How many more weeks will the class need to hold a bake sale to earn the remaining money to pay for the field trip? Show your work.

2 The school has decided that all 3 third-grade classes will go on the field trip to the science museum. The table shows the number of people in each class, including the teacher.

Class	Number of People (students and teacher)
Mrs. Nowak	22
Mrs. Olsen	24
Mr. Slattery	25

They can choose to use buses, vans, and cars to get to the museum. Buses have 20 seats, vans have 11 seats, and cars have 5 seats.

What combination of vehicles can be used to take all 3 classes on the field trip? Show your work.

3 Suppose that only 1 bus is available to use for the field trip. Now what combination of vehicles can be used to take all 3 classes on the field trip? Show your work.

4 There are 21 students in Mrs. Nowak's class. Six students tour the science museum with Mrs. Nowak. The remaining students are divided into 3 equal groups to tour the museum with a guide. How many students are in each group? Show your work.

5 The cost for visiting the museum is shown in the table. The admission price includes all regular exhibits at the museum. The dinosaur exhibit costs extra.

Kind of Visitor	Admission Price	Dinosaur Exhibit
Adult	$10	$5
Student	$8	$3
Children Age 0-5	$5	$0

Part A   What is the total cost of admission for Mrs. Nowak and her 21 students? Use estimation to check your answer for reasonableness. Show your work.

Part B   The museum also has a dinosaur exhibit that is only at the museum for a limited time. There is an extra charge to see the dinosaur exhibit. If 10 students also purchase a ticket to the dinosaur exhibit, what is the total cost for Mrs. Nowak and her class to visit the museum? Show your work.

Lesson 16

Domain: Operations and Algebraic Thinking
Cluster: Solve problems involving the four operations, and identify and explain patterns in arithmetic.
Standards: Primary 3.OA.9; Secondary 3.OA.5; Review 2.OA.3

Background Information:

Mrs. Norris's third grade class is working on finding patterns. Mrs. Norris has an addition table and a multiplication table displayed at the front of the classroom. The class is looking for patterns in each table.

Addition Table

+	0	1	2	3	4	5	6	7	8	9	10
0	0	1	2	3	4	5	6	7	8	9	10
1	1	2	3	4	5	6	7	8	9	10	11
2	2	3	4	5	6	7	8	9	10	11	12
3	3	4	5	6	7	8	9	10	11	12	13
4	4	5	6	7	8	9	10	11	12	13	14
5	5	6	7	8	9	10	11	12	13	14	15
6	6	7	8	9	10	11	12	13	14	15	16
7	7	8	9	10	11	12	13	14	15	16	17
8	8	9	10	11	12	13	14	15	16	17	18
9	9	10	11	12	13	14	15	16	17	18	19
10	10	11	12	13	14	15	16	17	18	19	20

Multiplication Table

×	0	1	2	3	4	5	6	7	8	9	10
0	0	0	0	0	0	0	0	0	0	0	0
1	0	1	2	3	4	5	6	7	8	9	10
2	0	2	4	6	8	10	12	14	16	18	20
3	0	3	6	9	12	15	18	21	24	27	30
4	0	4	8	12	16	20	24	28	32	36	40
5	0	5	10	15	20	25	30	35	40	45	50
6	0	6	12	18	24	30	36	42	48	54	60
7	0	7	14	21	28	35	42	49	56	63	70
8	0	8	16	24	32	40	48	56	64	72	80
9	0	9	18	27	36	45	54	63	72	81	90
10	0	10	20	30	40	50	60	70	80	90	100

1 Mrs. Norris asks you to start with a square for 1 in the addition table. She then asks you to shade a diagonal line from left to right, starting with the square for 1. Use the table above to shade a diagonal line as described. What do you notice about all the numbers in the diagonal line?

2 Mrs. Norris asks students to find whether the sum is even or odd when you add the following:

odd number + even number

odd number + odd number

even number + even number

Try different combinations of addends for each given situation. Look for patterns. Explain your findings.

3 Mrs. Norris uses the addition table to write these 2 addition sentences.

$$2 + 5 = 7 \qquad \text{and} \qquad 5 + 2 = 7$$

What pattern do you see? What addition property is shown by this pattern? Explain.

4 Mrs. Norris asks her students to shade all the multiples of 9 between 0 and 90 in the multiplication table. Shade the table as described. What do you notice about the sum of the digits in each multiple? How can this be useful?

5 Mrs. Norris shaded in a diagonal line on the multiplication table.

Multiplication Table

×	0	1	2	3	4	5	6	7	8	9	10
0	0	0	0	0	0	0	0	0	0	0	0
1	0	1	2	3	4	5	6	7	8	9	10
2	0	2	4	6	8	10	12	14	16	18	20
3	0	3	6	9	12	15	18	21	24	27	30
4	0	4	8	12	16	20	24	28	32	36	40
5	0	5	10	15	20	25	30	35	40	45	50
6	0	6	12	18	24	30	36	42	48	54	60
7	0	7	14	21	28	35	42	49	56	63	70
8	0	8	16	24	32	40	48	56	64	72	80
9	0	9	18	27	36	45	54	63	72	81	90
10	0	10	20	30	40	50	60	70	80	90	100

Part A   What do you notice about the products in the shaded squares?
Write multiplication sentences for the products in the shaded squares.
What do you notice about the factors?

Part B   Look again at the multiplication table and your findings in Part A.
Are your findings about the products and the factors true in other
diagonal lines that move up from left to right? Explain using a
multiplication property you know.

6 Mrs. Norris drew these tables on the board.

×	2	4	6	8	10
5					

×	1	3	5	7	9
5					

Complete each table. Describe a pattern you see in the products. Explain how patterns of the ones digits in the products relate to the factors.

Chapter 2

Number and Operations in Base Ten

Chapter 2 focuses on the domain Numbers and Operations in Base Ten. The chapter contains lessons. Each lesson covers a cluster and several of the Math Standards in that cluster. For some clusters, there are more than one lesson. The cluster covered in this chapter is listed below.

Cluster:

• Use place value understanding and properties of operations to perform multi-digit arithmetic.

Lesson 17

Domain: Number and Operations in Base Ten
Cluster: Use place value understanding and properties of operations to perform multi-digit arithmetic.
Standards: Primary 3.NBT.1; Secondary 3.OA.8, 3.NBT.3; Review 2.OA.3, 2.NBT.7

Background Information:

Businesses sometimes use rounding to tell about how many customers they have or about how many of each kind of product they sell.

Lori owns a gift shop. She records the number of customers who enter her store each day. The table shows her records for one week.

Gift Shop Customers

Day	Number of Customers
Sunday	782
Monday	667
Tuesday	429
Wednesday	583
Thursday	671
Friday	726
Saturday	867

1 Which two days had the fewest number of customers? Rounded to the nearest 10, about how many customers in all entered Lori's gift shop on these two days? Explain.

2 On which two days did about the same number of customers enter the store? Explain how to find the correct answer by rounding to the nearest 10.

3 Lori wants to know about how many customers in all entered her gift shop on Saturday and Sunday. Show how she can find the answer by rounding to the nearest 10.

4 Last week Lori's gift shop sold 60 get well cards. It sold twice as many congratulations cards and three times as many birthday cards. About how many cards did Lori's gift shop sell in all? Round your answer to the nearest 100.

5 Lori's gift shop sold an odd number of items yesterday. Rounding to the nearest hundred, she is able to round the number of items sold to 500. What is the least number of items that Lori's gift shop could have sold yesterday? What is the greatest number of items that Lori's gift shop could have sold yesterday?

6 Lori's gift shop is collecting canned goods for a food drive. The store's goal is to collect 300 cans of food. On the first day of the food drive, customers brought in 18 cans and employees brought in 27 cans.

Part A   About how many cans of food have been collected so far? Show your work.

Part B   The next day, customers bring in 16 cans. About how many cans of food still need to be collected to reach their goal? Show your work.

Lesson 18

Domain: Number and Operations in Base Ten
Cluster: Use place value understanding and properties of operations to perform multi-digit arithmetic.
Standards: Primary 3.NBT.2; Secondary 3.OA.8, 3.NBT.1; Review 2.NBT.6

Background Information:

If you have a bank account, you add money by making a deposit. You take money out of a bank account by making a withdrawal. A deposit increases the amount of money in the account. A withdrawal decreases the amount of money in the account. You can use addition and subtraction to keep track of the amount of money in the account.

1 Jared recorded the number of customers who opened a new bank account over the past three days.

| 12 | 15 | 18 |

He wrote this expression to find the total number of customers who opened a new account.

(12 + 15) + 18

Show how Jared can use the Associative Property of Addition and the Commutative Property of Addition to make solving this problem easier. How many customers opened a new bank account over the past 3 days?

2 In October, Naomi opened a bank account by depositing $247. During the same month, she deposited $132 and withdrew $65.

Part A   How much did Naomi have in her bank account at the end of October? Show your work.

Part B   In November, Naomi made deposits of $195 and $103. She also made withdrawals of $38 and $52. How much did Naomi have in her bank account at the end of November? Show your work.

3 The amount of money Adam deposited into his bank account for 3 months is shown in the table.

Month	Total Deposits
January	$403
February	$390
March	$515

Which two deposits total less than $800? Explain.

4 The amount Adam deposited in April is $230 less than the total amount deposited in February and March combined. How much did Adam deposit in April? Show your work.

5 A bank gives out lollipops to customers with children. Any lollipops left over at the end of the month are donated to a local charity. Last month, the bank donated 60 lollipops. This month the bank purchased 425 lollipops and gave out 388 lollipops. What is the difference between the number of lollipops donated last month and this month? Show your work.

6 Sarah planned to deposit $500 into her bank account each month during the summer. This would allow her to meet her goal for the entire summer. The table shows the total deposits Sarah actually made each month.

Month	Total Deposits
June	$543
July	$482
August	$429

By how much did Sarah miss her goal over the three-month period? Show your work.

Lesson 19

Domain: Number and Operations in Base Ten
Cluster: Use place value understanding and properties of operations to perform multi-digit arithmetic.
Standards: Primary 3.NBT.2; Secondary 3.OA.8, 3.NBT.1; Review 2.NBT.6

Background Information:

Many people collect favorite items. They use addition and subtraction to keep track of the number of items in their collections.

1 Komala collects seashells. The number sentence below shows the number of seashells she added and subtracted from her seashell collection. "START" is written below the number of seashells Komala started with and "END" is written beneath the number of seashells she has in her collection now. How many seashells did Komala start with? Show your work.

2 Trent has a collection of superhero cards. He gives 38 cards to his brother. He also gives 22 cards to his best friend. Trent has 125 cards left.

Part A   Explain how you can find the total number of superhero cards that Trent gave away. How many superhero cards did Trent give away?

Part B   How many superhero cards did Trent have before he gave some of them to his brother and best friend? Show your work.

3 Julius and Olivia collect coins. Julius has 338 coins in his collection. The number of coins Olivia has is 57 less than double the number of coins Julius has.

Part A   How many coins does Olivia have? Show your work.

Part B   Julius added 100 coins to his collection. How many more coins does he need to have the same amount as Olivia?

4 A zoo has a collection of birds and a collection of reptiles. The zoo has 570 birds and 295 reptiles. Use this information to answer questions 4 and 5.

Part A   Estimate the difference between the number of birds and the number of reptiles by rounding to the nearest hundred. Show your work.

Part B   The zoo owner needs to know exactly how many more birds the zoo has than reptiles. What is the difference between the number of birds and the number of reptiles at the zoo? Use your answer to Part A to explain if the answer you get for Part B seems reasonable.

Lesson 20

Domain: Number and Operations in Base Ten
Cluster: Use place value understanding and properties of operations to perform multi-digit arithmetic.
Standards: Primary 3.NBT.3; Secondary 3.OA.3, 3.OA.8, 3.NBT.2

Background Information:

The students and teachers at Dunmore Elementary are beginning a new school year. The following questions describe some events that take place at the school. Answering these questions will require multiplying with multiples of 10.

1 The school nurse is placing orders for supplies for the new school year. She has 3 boxes of bandages. There are 4 cartons of bandages in each box. Each carton has 30 bandages. The school nurse wants to have a supply of 600 bandages. How many more bandages should the school nurse order? Show your work.

2 The student council needs to set up 165 chairs so students can attend a presentation given by a guest speaker. So far they have set up 7 rows with 20 chairs in each row.

Part A   How many more chairs does the student council need to set up? Show your work.

Part B   The student council president just learned that some parents and members of the community would also like to hear the guest speaker. There is enough room to fit 3 more rows of chairs with 15 chairs in each row. How many more chairs can be set up in these 3 rows? How many chairs will be set up altogether? Show your work.

3 Dunmore Elementary is putting pads on the bottom of the chair and table legs. Each chair and each table has 4 legs. The pads keep the chairs and tables from scraping the floor when they are moved.

Part A   Last week the school put pads on all the legs of 30 chairs and 20 tables. What is the total number of pads that were placed on the chair and table legs last week? Show your work.

Part B   This week the school has put pads on the legs of 20 chairs and 10 tables. What is the total number of pads the school has placed on the chair and table legs during both weeks? Show your work.

4 During a math lesson, Layla writes the product of 4 and 70. Then, she subtracts the greatest two-digit multiple of 10 from the product. What is the difference between these numbers? Show your work.

5 The third grade students have set a goal to read a total of 200 books. Each student will read 5 books. Write and solve an equation to find the number of students in the third grade. Use a letter to stand for the unknown factor in the equation.

Chapter 3

Number and Operations —Fractions

Chapter 3 focuses on the domain Numbers and Operations— Fractions. The chapter contains lessons. Each lesson covers a cluster and several of the Math Standards in that cluster. For some clusters, there are more than one lesson. The cluster covered in this chapter is listed below.

Cluster:

• Develop understanding of fractions as numbers.

Lesson 21

Domain: Number and Operations—Fractions
Cluster: Develop understanding of fractions as numbers.
Standards: Primary 3.NF.1; Secondary 3.OA.3; Review 2.G.3

Background Information:

Jason likes to cook. He is planning a lasagna party for his friends. Help him plan how to serve equal portions of lasagna at the party.

1 Jason invites 7 friends to come to his house for dinner. He wants to make vegetable lasagna, but he is not sure how many friends will be able to attend.

Part A Jason and all 7 of his invited friends share the lasagna. Draw one way to cut the lasagna so that each person gets a piece that is equal in size. What fraction represents each person's share of the lasagna? Explain what the number in the numerator and the number in the denominator of the fraction represent.

Part B   Jason cannot decide whether to cut 1 row of 8 pieces or 2 rows of 4 pieces. Will each way represent the same fraction of the lasagna? Use words and drawings to explain why or why not.

Part C   At the last minute, one friend calls Jason to say that he cannot come to dinner. Jason already cut the lasagna, and each person eats one piece. What fraction of the lasagna did Jason and his friends eat? What fraction of the lasagna is left over? Draw a picture to show these fractions of the lasagna.

2 Shayla makes spinach lasagna for 4 people to share equally. Draw a rectangle to show one way that Shayla can cut 4 equal pieces. Write a fraction that names the whole lasagna. Then, shade 1 piece and write the fraction that it shows.

3 Jason and Shayla each made lasagna for their friends. Is $\frac{1}{2}$ of Jason's lasagna and $\frac{1}{2}$ of Shayla's lasagna the same amount? Explain when the answer might be yes and when it might be no.

4 At a pizza party, Caleb ate $\frac{3}{8}$ of a cheese pizza. Baylee ate $\frac{1}{4}$ of a mushroom pizza. Draw a circle for each pizza. Divide and shade one circle to show the fraction of pizza that Caleb ate. Divide and shade the other circle to show the fraction of pizza that Baylee ate. Label each pizza *Caleb* or *Baylee*.

5 Su Ling makes a large pizza that is a rectangle and wants to cut it into 12 equal parts. Show 3 different ways she can cut the pizza.

Lesson 22

Domain: Number and Operations—Fractions
Cluster: Develop understanding of fractions as numbers.
Standards: Primary 3.NF.1; Secondary 3.OA.3; Review 2.OA.3

Background Information:

Olivia uses small art tiles to make pictures of animals. The tiles are different shapes., She paints different patterns on some of the tiles. She also adds eyes, tails, and feet to her pictures. Some of her pictures are shown below.

1 Many of the tiles that Olivia used to make her animal pictures are shaded. Some of the tiles are not shaded. Olivia wants to write fractions that best represent the shaded portion of the tiles used to make each animal picture.

Part A   Look at the pictures of the animals that Olivia made using tiles. What fraction best expresses the shaded portion of tiles used to make each animal?

Bird: _____

Bug: _____

Dinosaur: _____

Giraffe: _____

Which animal picture was made using the greatest number of tiles that are equal in size?

Part B   Explain the meaning of each fraction that you wrote for the pictures. For each animal, tell how you found the top number (the numerator) and the bottom number (the denominator).

Part C   Which two animal pictures could you use to show $\frac{1}{2}$? Use a division sentence to explain how they each show $\frac{1}{2}$.

2 Olivia makes another bug picture. She wants to use round tiles that are shaded and round tiles that are <u>not</u> shaded. She will use 3 tiles. Can she make a bug that shows $\frac{1}{2}$? Explain why or why not.

3 Look again at the bird picture that is made using 4 tiles. Draw a line through each tile to make 2 equal triangles. How many equal triangles are in the bird now? What fraction of all the tiles is shown by the white triangles?

4　Olivia gives the giraffe picture to Tasha. Tasha wants to use craft sticks to make a frame around the picture. The picture is 1 craft stick wide and 2 craft sticks tall.

Part A　There are three different types of craft sticks that Tasha can use to make a frame:

- gray
- white
- half gray and half white

Circle 6 craft sticks below that will make a frame that is $\frac{1}{2}$ gray and $\frac{1}{2}$ white. Draw the frame to show how you can place the craft sticks.

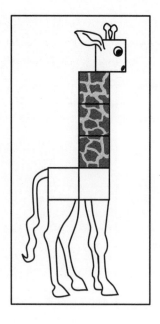

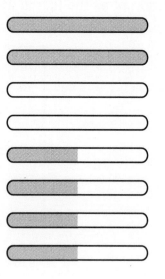

Part B   Tasha changes her mind and wants to make a frame that is $\frac{1}{3}$ gray and $\frac{2}{3}$ white. Circle the craft sticks that she can use. Draw the frame to show how you can place the craft sticks.

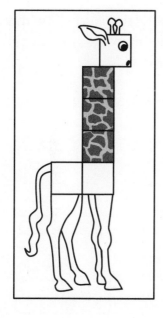
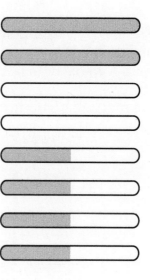

Lesson 23

Domain: Number and Operations—Fractions
Cluster: Develop understanding of fractions as numbers.
Standards: Primary 3.NF.2a; Secondary 3.OA.1, 3.NF.3d

Background Information:

Mr. Fincher teaches music. He writes a measure of a musical melody. The measure has a beginning bar and an ending bar. The symbol shown in the measure is called a whole note. A whole note lasts for one whole measure.

Beneath the measure of music is a number line that helps to show the length of a whole note.

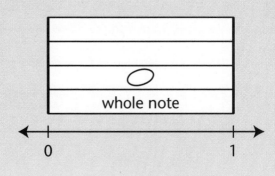

1 Mr. Fincher draws more measures and number lines. Use his drawings to answer the following questions.

Part A   The drawing shows two notes that fill the measure. They are called half notes. Explain how the measure of music and the number line show halves. Then write the missing fraction that is on the number line.

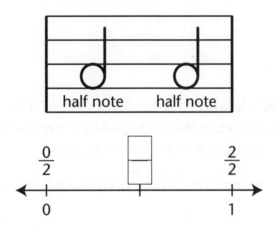

Part B   The drawing shows four quarter notes that fill the measure. Each quarter note is $\frac{1}{4}$ of the measure. Complete the number line drawing to show the same equal parts as the quarter notes show. Then, label the fractions for the dividing lines that you draw on the number line.

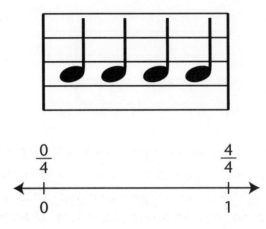

Part C   Mr. Fincher gives his students a challenge for fun. He draws a longer measure with just one note on it. He calls it an eighth note. If an eighth note is $\frac{1}{8}$ of the measure, how can you show eighths with notes and a number line? Draw the notes to finish the measure. Then, complete the number line to show how to count the notes by eighths. Label each fraction on the number line.

2 In school, Kelvin learned about a quarter note, a quarter hour, a quarter of a dollar, and a quarter of an inch. Explain how each of these is similar to finding $\frac{1}{4}$ on a number line?

3 Jenny thinks that a quarter note lasts longer than a half note. She says that 4 is greater than 2. William thinks that a half note lasts longer than a quarter note. He says that a measure divided by 2 has longer equal parts than a measure divided by 4. Draw two number lines to show quarters and halves. Then tell who is correct and why.

4 Landon's favorite activity is his guitar lesson every Tuesday after school. It lasts $\frac{2}{3}$ of an hour each week. Is that longer than or shorter than $\frac{1}{3}$ of an hour? Draw a number line to show $\frac{1}{3}$ and $\frac{2}{3}$. Label the fractions and circle the one that shows the longer time.

5 Angela, Michael, and Danika are all using the same book for their piano lessons. The book has 6 lessons. Angela has completed $\frac{3}{6}$ of the book. Michael has completed 2 more lessons than Angela. Danika has completed the first lesson in the book. Mark the number line below to show the fractions of the book that each piano student has completed. Then, write each piano student's name and draw a line from each name to the matching fraction on the number line.

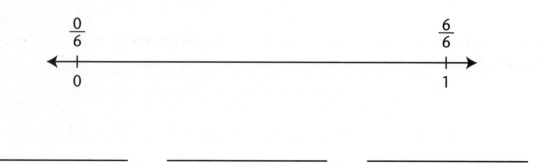

_____   _____   _____

Lesson 24

Domain: Number and Operations—Fractions
Cluster: Develop understanding of fractions as numbers.
Standards: Primary 3.NF.2b; Secondary 3.G.2; Review 2.MD.2, 2.MD.6

Background Information:

Beans and peas grow in pods that are long and thin. When the pods are ripe, you can count their length by the number of beans or peas inside.

1 Victor picks some green bean pods from his garden. He makes a drawing to show how bean pods are like number lines.

Part A   Look at the green bean pod below and the number lines. The first number line counts the beans that are inside the pod. Write the missing numbers. The second number line shows one pod and the fractions of equal parts. Write the missing fractions on the number line.

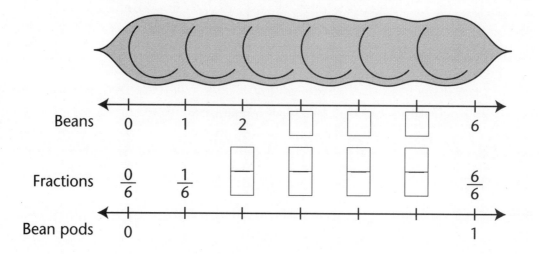

Part B   Compare the number lines in Part A. What fraction of the whole pod does 1 bean show? How does counting the beans help you find the numerators and denominators of the fractions in the whole bean pod?

2 Emma picks some lima bean pods from her garden. The picture shows a lima bean pod that is open. Complete the number line to show 1 whole pod and the fractions of the pod that the beans show. Mark the number line in equal parts. Write the fractions where they belong above the number line.

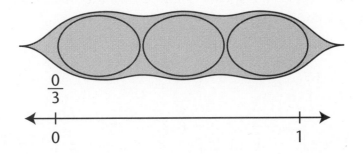

$\dfrac{0}{3}$

0   1

3 Kojo buys some green pea pods at a farmers' market. Kojo opens one of the pods and sees 4 peas inside. Complete two number lines to count the peas and to show the whole pod divided into the fractions that the peas represent.

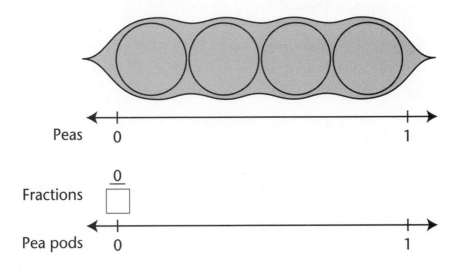

Peas   0   1

Fractions $\dfrac{0}{\square}$

Pea pods   0   1

4 A green pea is about as wide as your pinky finger. A lima bean is about as wide as your thumb. Which would be longer, a green pea pod with 5 peas or a lima bean pod with 5 beans? Use words and drawings to explain your answer.

5 A peanut is a pea, but it is not a nut. In fact, some people call them goober peas. Most peanut pods, called shells, have 1, 2, or 3 peanuts inside. If peanuts grow in pods like other peas, how many peanuts do you think are in the peanut shell below? Complete the number line to show that there is 1 peanut shell. Mark the parts of the number line to show the fraction of the shell that each peanut shows.

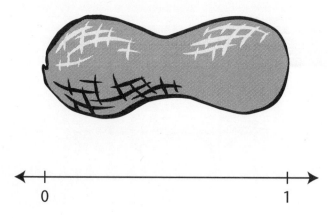

0   1

6   Draw a pea pod that has 8 peas. Draw a number line under it that counts the peas
by whole numbers. Then, draw another number line to show one whole pod and
the fractions that the peas represent. Be sure to mark the number lines in equal
sections and write all of the whole numbers and fractions.

Lesson 25

Domain: Number and Operations—Fractions
Cluster: Develop understanding of fractions as numbers.
Standards: Primary 3.NF.3a, 3.NF.3b; Secondary 3.G.2; Review 2.MD.6

Background Information:

Nadia and Fargo own a store called The Beads and Brads Bazaar. They make and sell jewelry, belts, and many other decorations. They are getting ready to sell some items at a craft fair.

1 Nadia makes some jewelry to sell at the fair. She wants to make some adult bracelets that are the same length. The beads come in different sizes. Use the pictures to answer questions about the bracelets.

Part A   Compare the two bracelets shown below. For each bracelet, write the fraction of the bracelet that is shown by 1 bead. Then, write the fraction that represents half of each bracelet.

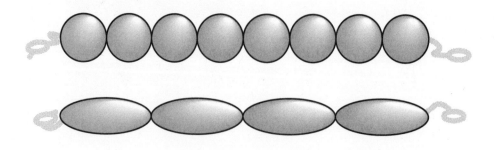

Part B Nadia plans to make a few bracelets for children. The children's bracelets are $\frac{3}{4}$ the length of the adult bracelets. Look at the adult bracelets and number lines below. Circle the fraction on each number line that represents $\frac{3}{4}$ of the length. How many beads long will Nadia make each of the children's bracelets using these size beads?

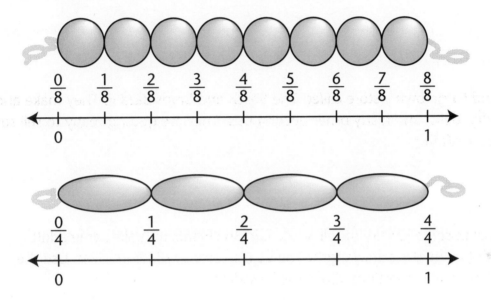

Part C Use the number lines above to write the equivalent fractions that are shown. Use an equals sign between each pair of fractions. Explain how you know they are equivalent.

2 Fargo is making brad designs on leather belts for the craft fair. He uses some oval brads and round brads that are silver.

Part A Compare the rows of brads shown below. Write the fraction that represents one-third of each row. Then, write the fraction that represents two-thirds of each row.

Part B Explain how the number lines show equivalent fractions. Do they show equivalent fractions for $\frac{1}{2}$? Tell why or why not.

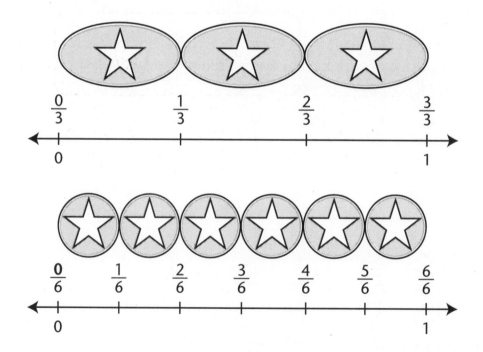

3 Nadia and Fargo also make belt buckles. The two favorite styles are the hexagon and octagon buckles. Nadia and Fargo glue triangle tiles onto these shapes to make different designs.

Part A   Color the tiles in the hexagon buckles to show $\frac{1}{2}$, $\frac{1}{3}$, and $\frac{2}{3}$. Write an equivalent fraction that each buckle shows.

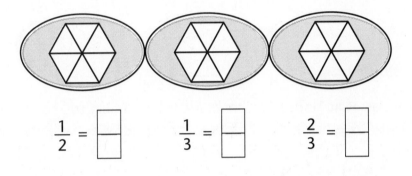

$$\frac{1}{2} = \boxed{}\qquad \frac{1}{3} = \boxed{}\qquad \frac{2}{3} = \boxed{}$$

Part B   Color the tiles in the octagon buckles to show $\frac{1}{2}$, $\frac{1}{4}$, and $\frac{3}{4}$. Write an equivalent fraction that each buckle shows.

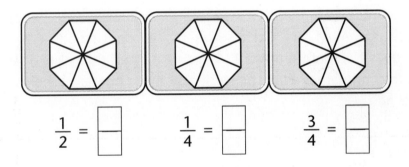

$$\frac{1}{2} = \boxed{}\qquad \frac{1}{4} = \boxed{}\qquad \frac{3}{4} = \boxed{}$$

Lesson 26

Domain: Number and Operations—Fractions
Cluster: Develop understanding of fractions as numbers.
Standards: Primary 3.NF.3c; Secondary 3.NF.3a, 3.NF.2a, 3.OA.7

Background Information:

The third grade classes at Northlake School are taking a field trip to an amusement park. They will stay together in small groups. Each group will have adult helpers along with them.

1 Mrs. Garza has a group of 8 students. The students look for a ride that they can all ride at the same time.

Part A The students find a boat that swings back and forth. Four people will fit on each side. All of Mrs. Garza's students get on the boat. What fraction of riders does 1 student represent? What fraction of riders sits on each side? What fraction names all of the students on the boat and shows that the boat is full?

Part B Complete the number line to show the fractions represented by the students on the boat ride. What whole number is equivalent to the fraction that represents 8 students? Does this number tell you the number of students on the ride, the number of groups on the boat, or the number of groups waiting in line? How do you know?

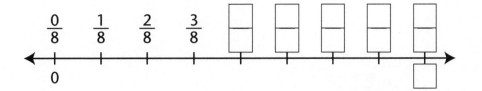

Part C When the students get off of the boat ride, one of them says that only a fraction of them are there. Then, he says that the fraction is $\frac{8}{1}$. He laughs, but some others do not get the joke and look around to see who is missing. Explain how many students are represented by the fraction $\frac{8}{1}$ and why someone might mistakenly think some students are missing.

113

2 Mr. Yeh has a group of 4 boys that he is helping at the amusement park. They go on many water rides. Mr. Yeh goes on some of the rides with them.

Part A   The boys want to go on the log ride. They know they will get splashed with water and want to cool off from the hot day. They ask Mr. Yeh to ride with them. The group that rides can be described by the fraction $\frac{4}{4}$. Does that mean that Mr. Yeh joins the boys or not? Explain how you know.

Part B   Mr. Yeh joins his group to ride in a raft. It spins as it flows down a water lane and over the rapids. What fraction can he use to name the number of people who are in the raft? What can you do to name any whole number as a fraction?

3 Some of the school groups join together to ride on a roller coaster. Twelve people can ride in 4 cars, 9 people can ride in 3 cars, and 6 people can ride in 2 cars. Mrs. Hall says that the fractions of people and cars are $\frac{12}{4}$, $\frac{9}{3}$, and $\frac{6}{2}$. What is the fraction that represents how many people can ride in 1 car? What is the whole number that names all of these equivalent fractions? Show your work.

4 The next day at school, Mrs. Hall uses number lines to tell her students more about fractions. She draws number lines to review fractions on the swinging boat ride, the log ride, and the roller coaster. Look at the point that is marked on each number line below. What do these points have in common?

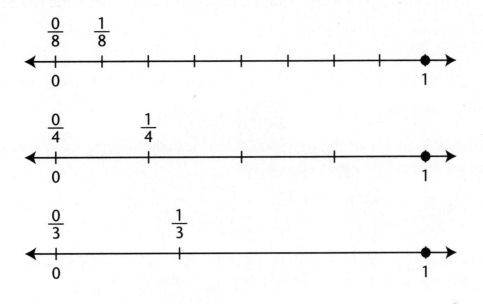

Lesson 27

Domain: Number and Operations—Fractions
Cluster: Develop understanding of fractions as numbers.
Standards: Primary 3.NF.3d; Secondary 3.G.2; Review 2.G.3

Background Information:

Some friends sign up for an after-school quilting class. In the first lesson, they cut many squares of cloth that are the same size.

---

1 Sandy cuts squares to make many designs. Some of the squares are solid colors and some are not. She makes different groupings of the squares.

Part A   Sandy sews together 8 squares to begin her quilt. Look at her pattern below. Write the fraction that names the shaded part. Write a fraction that names the white part. Then, write a math sentence to compare the fractions. Use >, =, or < between the fractions to show the comparison.

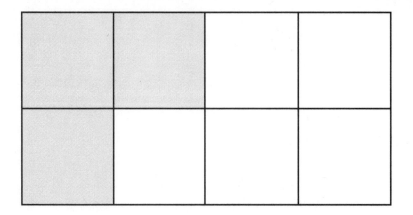

Part B Sandy uses 4 of her squares to make a larger square. Use the picture below that shows the larger square. Write a fraction that names the white part. Write a fraction that names the dotted part. Then, write a math sentence to compare the fractions. Use >, =, or < between the fractions to show the comparison.

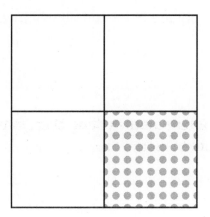

Part C Sandy sews together some of her squares to show that $\frac{2}{3} > \frac{1}{3}$. Is Sandy's comparison correct? Draw what Sandy's quilt parts might look like.

2 Marco sews together his squares to make different designs. Some of his designs are rectangles. Some of them make diamond patterns.

Part A   Marco sews 4 of his squares together to make a larger square. He says that the larger square shows that $\frac{1}{4} < \frac{1}{2}$. Is Marco correct? How does the drawing of his larger square below prove whether his conclusion is true or false?

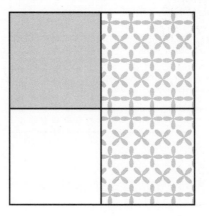

Part B   Marco sews 6 squares together to make a diamond pattern. He uses the same size squares to sew 8 squares together. He says that the diamond patterns show that $\frac{1}{6} = \frac{1}{8}$. What is the problem with Marco's conclusion? Write a comparison that is true about $\frac{1}{6}$ and $\frac{1}{8}$.

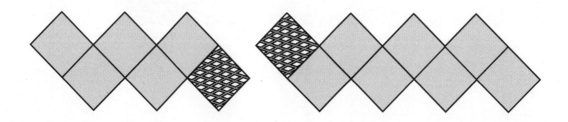

3 In the third quilting lesson, the teacher shows how to use triangles to sew together hexagons and octagons.

Part A Minay makes two hexagons with her triangle pieces. Look at Minay's hexagon designs below. Write a number in the box to complete each fraction that is shown. Then, write a fraction comparison for the fractions using the symbol >, =, or <.

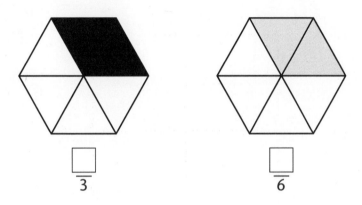

$$\frac{\square}{3} \qquad \frac{\square}{6}$$

Part B Jack makes two octagons with his triangle pieces. He says that the octagons show that $\frac{2}{8}$ is greater than $\frac{1}{4}$. Is Jack correct? Explain your answer and write a comparison that is true.

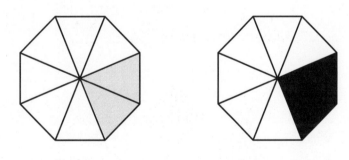

Chapter 4

Measurement and Data

Chapter 4 focuses on the domain Measurement and Data. The chapter contains lessons. Each lesson covers a cluster and several of the Math Standards in that cluster. For some clusters, there are more than one lesson. The clusters covered in this chapter are listed below.

Clusters:

• Solve problems involving measurement and estimation of intervals of time, liquid volumes, and masses of objects.

• Represent and interpret data.

• Geometric measurement: understand concepts of area and relate area to multiplication and to addition.

• Geometric measurement: recognize perimeter as an attribute of plane figures and distinguish between linear and area measures.

Lesson 28

Domain: Measurement and Data
Cluster: Solve problems involving measurement and estimation of intervals of time, liquid volumes, and masses of objects.
Standards: Primary 3.MD.1; Secondary 3.OA.8; Review 2.MD.7

Background Information:

Justin is going to spend a week visiting his mom's sister. Aunt Donna plans to take Justin some places that she thinks her 9-year-old nephew will like.

1 Aunt Donna makes a chart to show what they will do on Monday. She draws clocks to show the schedule. Use the schedule to answer the questions.

MONDAY				
Wake up	Cave tour	Movie starts	Movie ends	Dinner

Part A   Aunt Donna sets the alarm clock for the time they need to get up on Monday. If Justin gets up at 8:05, is he early or late? How many minutes early or late is Justin? Explain how you know.

Part B   Justin and Aunt Donna go to the Cave Museum. They arrive 10 minutes before the tour starts. The tour lasts an hour and a half. What time do they arrive at the Cave Museum? What time does the tour begin and end?

Part C   After the tour, Justin and his aunt go to lunch. Then they go to a movie theater. List the times that the movie begins and ends. Is it longer than or shorter than 2 hours long? How do you know?

2 On some days, Justin and his aunt go swimming. A walk to the pool takes 13 minutes. The clock shows what time they start walking to the pool on Wednesday. Write the time below the first clock. Then draw hands on the second clock to show what time they get to the pool. Write the time below the second clock.

3 Aunt Donna takes Justin to a special animal park on Friday. They use a schedule of shows to plan their day. Each show lasts 1 hour.

Shows	Morning	Early Afternoon	Late Afternoon
Splashing Sea Lions	9:45	12:35	3:20
Rocking Rodeo	10:05	2:30	none
Trained Toucans	10:15	2:15	4:15
Underwater Wonders	11:30	12:45	4:10

Part A   Justin wants to see late afternoon shows for the Splashing Sea Lions and the Trained Toucans. Is this possible? Explain why or why not.

Part B Justin and his aunt are getting on a train ride that goes around the park. The ride begins and ends beside the theater for the underwater show. The ride takes 35 minutes. Look at the current time that is shown on the watch below. What is the earliest time they can go to see the Underwater Wonders? Explain.

Part C The clock below shows the time that Justin and Aunt Donna buy their lunch. What is the time on the clock? What early afternoon shows will they choose between? Explain your thinking.

Lesson 29

Domain: Measurement and Data
Cluster: Solve problems involving measurement and estimation of intervals of time, liquid volumes, and masses of objects.
Standards: Primary 3.MD.1; Secondary 3.NBT.2; Review 2.OA.1

Background Information:

A track and field contest is very organized. Each event happens on a schedule. Each team must be on time to compete.

1   Coach Addison tells his team to meet in the gym a few minutes past 7:00 A.M. for a warm up. After the warm up, they will walk to the field and get ready for the early races of the day. The coach makes a number line to show the morning schedule.

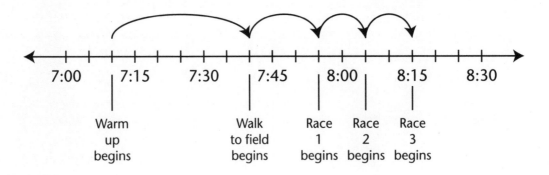

  ©RALLY! EDUCATION. No part of this document may be reproduced without written permission from the publisher.

Part A   Use the number line to find the time that the warm up, the walk to the field, and Race 1 begin. Write the times. Write the number of minutes between each of these times. How many minutes pass from the beginning of the warm up to the beginning of Race 1? Did you use addition, subtraction, or the number line?

Part B   By 8:15 A.M., all 3 of the morning races are going on at the same time. Race 2 ends 44 minutes after it begins. Write the times that it begins and ends.

Part C   Race 1 lasts 45 minutes. Race 3 ends 29 minutes after it begins. Which race ends first, middle, and last? Mark and label the ending times of each race on the number line below to show your work.

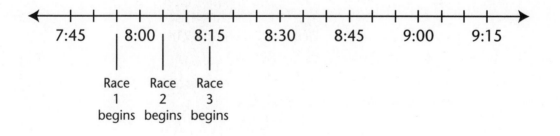

2 Coach Vasquez gets her team ready for the afternoon events. She shows them the starting times on a number line.

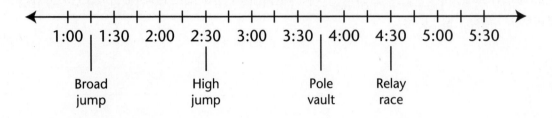

1:00   1:30   2:00   2:30   3:00   3:30   4:00   4:30   5:00   5:30

Broad jump   High jump   Pole vault   Relay race

Part A   Write the time that each event begins.

Part B   How many minutes apart does each event begin?

3 One race begins at 1:05 in the afternoon. The first runner crosses the finish line in 7 minutes. The last runner crosses the finish line in 11 minutes. Draw a number line to show the starting time and the ending times for the first and last runners. Be sure to label the times.

4 One track event begins at 3:15 and ends at 4:05. Orlando wants to show this on a number line. Should he mark the number line in intervals of 1 minute, 5 minutes, or 15 minutes? Explain or make a drawing to tell why you think so.

Lesson 30

Domain: Measurement and Data
Cluster: Solve problems involving measurement and estimation of intervals of time, liquid volumes, and masses of objects.
Standards: Primary 3.MD.2; Secondary 3.OA.3; Review 2.OA.1

Background Information:

Renata studies all kinds of creatures. She uses information about the mass of each creature to make comparisons.

1 Renata uses a balance scale to compare mass. She uses grams and kilograms on the scale.

Part A   If the mass of Renata's jar is 1,000 grams, what is the mass of the bee inside the jar? Explain how you can tell.

Part B   Use the picture of the scales to find the mass of the mouse and the mass of the rat. Which one has a greater mass?

Part C   Compare the items on the scales. Which two items have the same mass? How do you know?

2 Renata has a pet that has a mass of 10 kilograms. Another pet has a mass of 10 grams. One of the pets is a small lizard, and one is a dog. Which pet has each mass? Which pet has the least mass? Why?

3 Billy has a large cat that eats 200 grams of canned food every day. How many days does it take for the cat to eat 1,000 grams of canned food? How many days does it take for the cat to eat 2 kilograms of canned food? Explain how you found the answer in kilograms.

4 Lamont says that his new kitten has a mass of about 200 kilograms. He says that his pet parrot has a mass of about 20 kilograms. Do you think that Lamont's estimates are reasonable or not? Explain why you think so.

5 Cara has 2 large dogs. The sum of their masses is 50 kilograms. The difference of their masses is 4 kilograms. What is the mass of each dog?

Lesson 31

Domain: Measurement and Data
Cluster: Solve problems involving measurement and estimation of intervals of time,
liquid volumes, and masses of objects.
Standards: Primary 3.MD.2; Secondary 3.OA.3; Review 2.OA.1

Background Information:

Some Little League baseball teams play in parks that have a snack stand.

1 There is a snack stand behind the Greenville Park baseball field. It sells 1-liter and 2-liter bottles of water. It also sells small and large sizes of juice. The workers measure $\frac{1}{2}$ liter for a small juice and 1 liter for a large juice. The sign below shows the drinks that are for sale.

Part A   Mrs. Tomlinson sells 5 bottles of 1-liter water and 5 bottles of 2-liter water. How many total liters of water does Mrs. Tomlinson sell? Show your work.

Part B   Mr. Drake sells 12 liters of juice during a game. Each order is for a small juice. How many small juices does he sell? Show your work.

Part C   Mr. Chung sells 6 small juices and 11 large juices. How many total liters of juice does he sell? Explain how you found your answer.

2 Coach Wojak brings water for her team. She fills a large ice chest with 1-liter bottles of water. What is the most reasonable estimate for the total amount of water: 3 liters, 30 liters, 300 liters, or 3,000 liters? Explain your answer.

3 The snack stand began the day with 48 liters of orange juice and 44 liters of apple juice. At the end of the day, there were 12 liters of juice left. How many liters of juice were sold? Show the steps you used to solve the problem.

4 Mr. Marsh sold 25 liters of orange juice, 25 liters of apple juice, and 25 liters of water. How many total liters did he sell? Explain how you found your answer.

5 Ms. Sutton sold a case of 1-liter bottles of water. The case had 4 rows of 8 bottles each in it. Draw an array to show the total number of liters of water that were in the case.

Lesson 32

Domain: Measurement and Data
Cluster: Represent and interpret data.
Standards: Primary 3.MD.3; Secondary 3.OA.3; Review 2.OA.1

Background Information:

A bookstore manager collects information about sales. He creates graphs to make it easier to see the sales records.

1 Tonya helps her manager collect information for the bookstore. She makes a picture graph to show the sales for one Saturday.

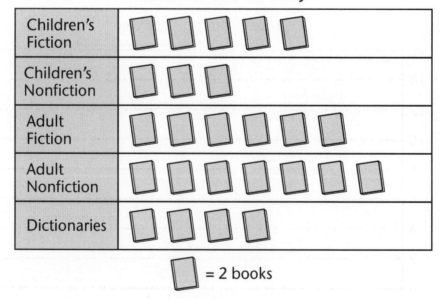

Part A   How many more adult books than children's books were sold?
Show your work.

Part B   How many fewer dictionaries were sold than fiction books?
Show your work.

Part C   Look at Tonya's picture graph. Complete the bar graph below to
show another way to display the book sales.

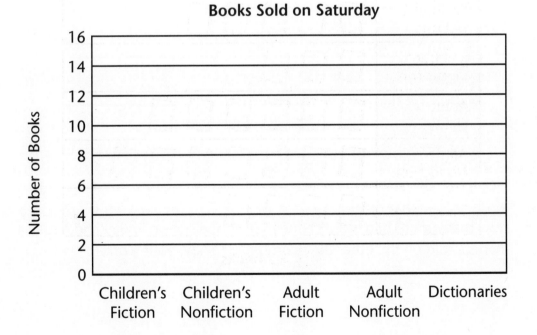

Books Sold on Saturday

2 Darnell made a list of the number of books that he sold over five days.

Darnell's Book Sales

Day	Number of Books Sold
Tuesday	15
Wednesday	10
Thursday	20
Friday	35
Saturday	25

Part A   Complete a picture graph to show the data about the books that Darnell sold. Use the scale that is given below the picture graph.

Darnell's Book Sales

Tuesday	
Wednesday	
Thursday	
Friday	
Saturday	

= 5 books

Part B   How many more books did Darnell sell altogether on Friday and Saturday than he sold on the other days combined? Show your work.

3 The bookstore manager needs 18 cookbooks, 12 dictionaries, 21 joke books, and 9 crafts books. He gives Darnell a picture graph that shows what to order.

Part A   Complete the picture graph to show the book order. Use the scale that is given.

Books to Order

Cookbooks	
Dictionaries	
Joke Books	
Crafts Books	

= 3 books

Part B   What scale did the manager use to make his picture graph? Explain why you think he used that scale.

Lesson 33

Domain: Measurement and Data
Cluster: Represent and interpret data.
Standards: Primary 3.MD.3; Secondary 3.OA.3; Review 2.OA.1

Background Information:

Forest rangers gather information about the animals that live in wildlife parks.
They list the types of animals and the numbers of each type.

---

1 Ranger Travis makes a bar graph to show data about the animals that he observes on one of his walks.

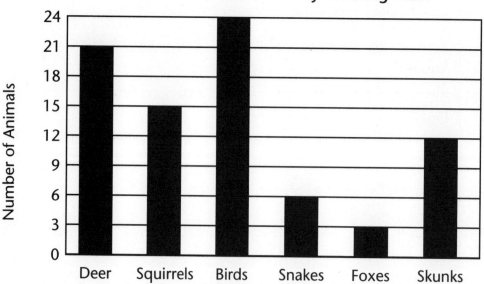

Part A   How many more birds does Ranger Travis observe than snakes, foxes, and skunks combined? Show your work.

Part B   Which two groups of animals can be combined to match the number of deer that Ranger Travis counted? Explain how you solved the problem.

Part C   Use Ranger Travis' bar graph. Complete the picture graph below to show another way to display the information about the forest animals. Be sure to include a number in your scale.

Animals Counted on Monday Morning Walk

Deer	
Squirrels	
Birds	
Snakes	
Foxes	
Skunks	

⬤ = _____ animals

2 Ranger Camille made a list of the animals that she counted in her wildlife park in a day. She estimated each number to the nearest ten.

Animals Counted in One Day

Animal	Number Counted
Rabbits	about 20
Elk	about 40
Deer	about 30
Bears	about 10
Birds	about 60

Part A Complete the bar graph to show the data about the animals that Ranger Camille counted.

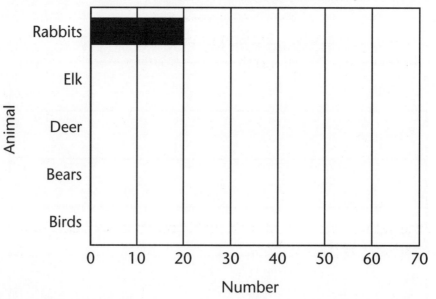

Animals Counted in One Day

Part B Are there more rabbits and deer altogether or elk and bears altogether? Explain your comparison.

3 Ranger Keiko makes a bar graph for the forest vet. It shows the number of animals that were treated last year.

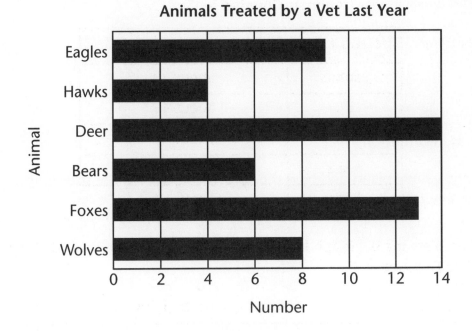

Animals Treated by a Vet Last Year

Part A   How many bears, wolves, and foxes were treated by the vet? Explain how you found each number and the sum. Show your work.

Part B   Did the vet treat fewer birds or deer? Show your work and write the comparison using a < symbol.

Lesson 34

Domain: Measurement and Data
Cluster: Represent and interpret data.
Standards: Primary 3.MD.4; Secondary 3.NF.2; Review 2.MD.1

Background Information:

Some scientists study plants and how they grow. They record the sizes of the plants at different stages of growth and compare the data.

1 Cho measures some leaves and counts how many are on each small plant.
Then he makes line plots to show the data that he collects.

Part A   Measure the length of each leaf to the nearest $\frac{1}{4}$ of an inch. Then write
the lengths in order from shortest to longest.

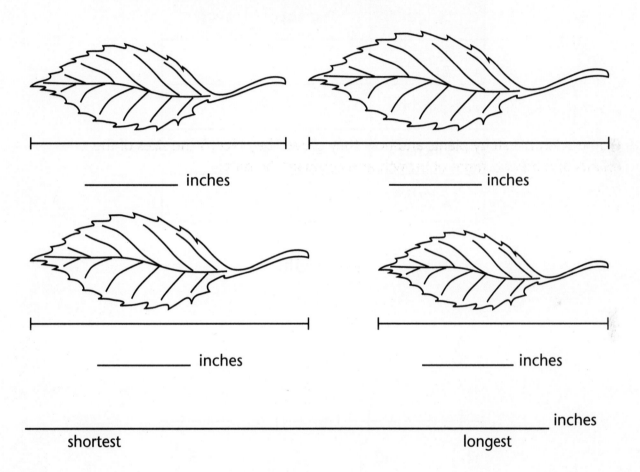

_____ inches   _____ inches

_____ inches   _____ inches

_____ inches
       shortest   longest

Part B Cho counts the number of leaves that he has for each length. He makes a list and begins a line plot. Use Cho's list to complete the line plot.

Leaf Lengths

Length	Number of Leaves
$2\frac{1}{2}$ inches	4
$2\frac{3}{4}$ inches	3
3 inches	6
$3\frac{1}{4}$ inches	2

Leaf Lengths

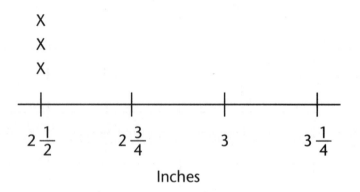

Inches

Part C What are the lengths of the fewest leaves and the most leaves? How does a line plot help you compare the numbers of leaves?

2 Paige plants some beans and measures the heights of the bean sprouts after 4 weeks. She makes a chart to show her work.

Part A   Measure each plant to the nearest quarter inch. Write the measurements in the chart.

Heights of Bean Sprouts

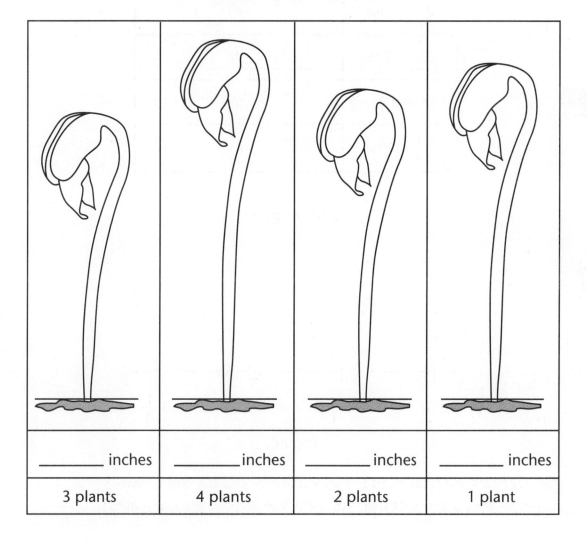

_____ inches	_____ inches	_____ inches	_____ inches
3 plants	4 plants	2 plants	1 plant

151

Part B   Complete the line plot to show the data that is in Paige's chart.

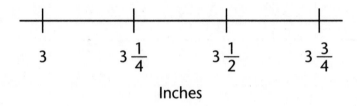

$$3 \qquad 3\frac{1}{4} \qquad 3\frac{1}{2} \qquad 3\frac{3}{4}$$

Inches

3 Luke compares the heights of the bushes in his yard. He measures the bushes to the nearest half inch. Then he makes a line plot to show his data.

Heights of Bushes

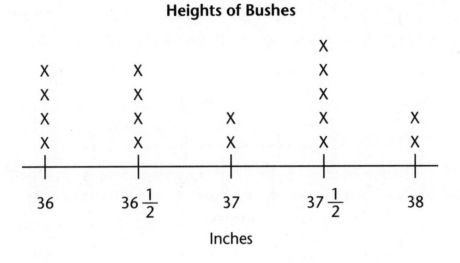

Inches

Part A   How many bushes are in Luke's yard? Explain how you know.

Part B   Does Luke have more bushes that are shorter than or taller than 37 inches? Show your work.

Lesson 35

Domain: Measurement and Data
Cluster: Represent and interpret data.
Standards: Primary 3.MD.4; Secondary 3.NF.2; Review 2.MD.1

> **Background Information:**
>
> There are buttons for clothes and coats. There are also buttons for decorations. The styles and sizes of buttons depend on how they are going to be used.

1 Marissa sorts a collection of buttons. She measures the buttons to think about how she can use them. She makes line plots to compare how many buttons she has of many sizes.

Part A   Measure the width of each button to the nearest $\frac{1}{4}$ inch. Then write the widths in order from shortest to longest.

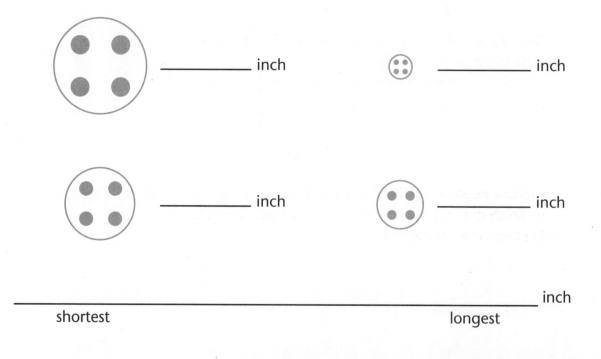

_____ inch   _____ inch

_____ inch   _____ inch

_____ inch
shortest   longest

Part B   Marissa counts the number of buttons that she has for each size.
         She makes a list. Use Marissa's list to complete the line plot.

Button Widths

Width	Number of Buttons
$\frac{1}{4}$ inch	3
$\frac{1}{2}$ inch	7
$\frac{3}{4}$ inch	6
1 inch	4

Button Widths

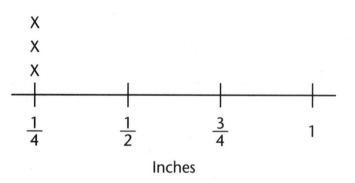

Inches

Part C   Marissa needs 4 of the smallest buttons and 6 of the half-inch buttons
         to finish making a shirt. Does she have enough of these buttons?
         Explain why or why not.

2 Antonio buys some special buttons to make some pillows. He buys 3 buttons that are $1\frac{1}{2}$ inches wide and 5 buttons that are $1\frac{3}{4}$ inches wide. He buys 6 buttons that are 2 inches wide and 1 button that is $2\frac{1}{4}$ inches wide.

Part A   Make a line plot to show the buttons that Antonio buys.

Antonio's Buttons

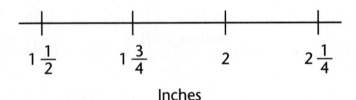

Inches

Part B   Does Antonio buy more buttons that are at least 2 inches wide or more buttons that are smaller than 2 inches? Show your work. Use the > symbol to write the comparison of the sums.

3 Kalenda sorts a collection of buttons. Measure the buttons to the nearest half inch.
Then make a line plot to show how many buttons there are of each width.

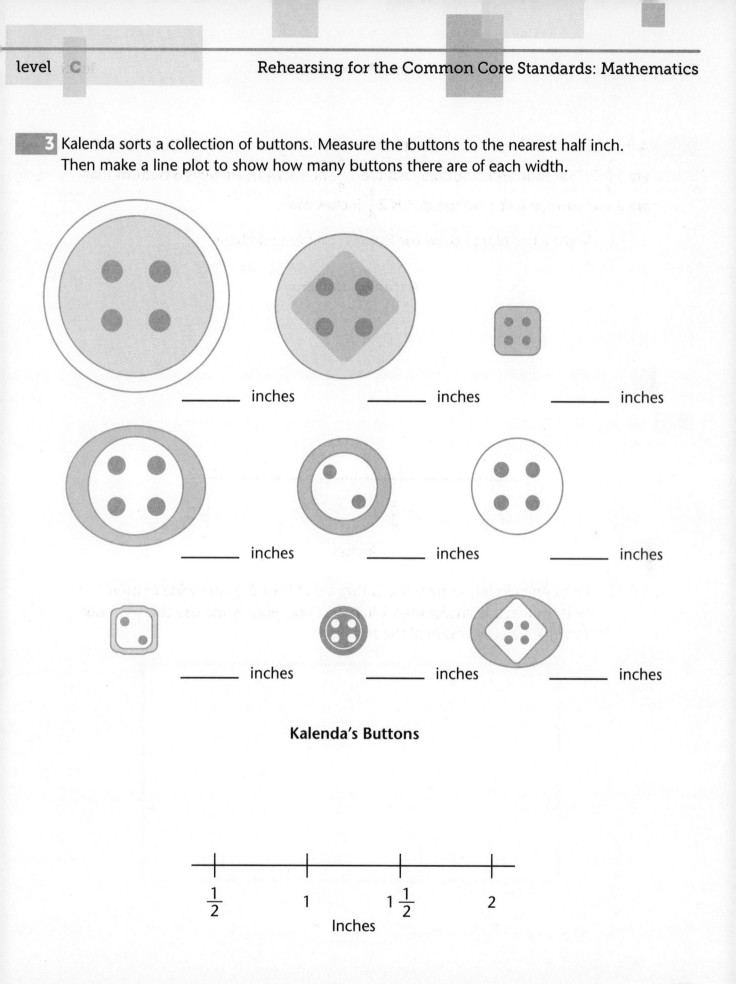

_____ inches   _____ inches   _____ inches

_____ inches   _____ inches   _____ inches

_____ inches   _____ inches   _____ inches

Kalenda's Buttons

$\frac{1}{2}$ 1 $1\frac{1}{2}$ 2

Inches

Lesson 36

Domain: Measurement and Data
Cluster: Geometric measurement: understand concepts of area and relate area to multiplication and to addition.
Standards: Primary 3.MD.5a, 3.MD.5b; Secondary 3.G.2; Review 2.G.2

Background Information:

Mr. and Mrs. Morales build homes. They use square tiles for some of the floors.

1 Mr. Morales puts tile floors in some closets. Help him count the number of square tiles he uses. One tile is shown below.

 = 1 square floor tile (1 square unit)

Part A The drawing shows one of the closet floors that Mr. Morales has covered. Shade 1 square unit. How many square tiles cover the area? Write the number that completes the sentence.

The area of the closet floor is _____ square units.

Part B Two closet floors are shown below. Mr. Morales has placed 1 tile in each closet. Which closet floor covers the most area? How can you tell?

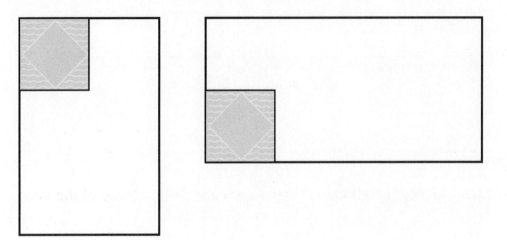

Part C The linen closet is 3 square units long and 3 square units wide. Draw the tiles inside the figure below. Write the number that completes the sentence.

The area of the closet floor is _____ square units.

2 Mrs. Morales uses large cement tiles to make some patio areas outdoors.

Part A   How many tiles does Mrs. Morales use on the patio that is shown below?
Write the number that completes the sentence.

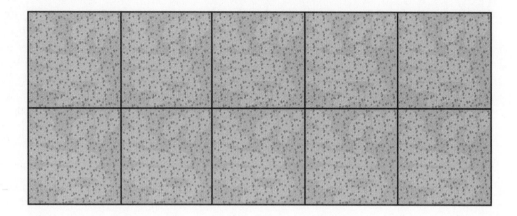

The area of the patio is _____ square units.

Part B   Mrs. Morales makes another patio area. Does this one have the same area
as the first one? Explain why or why not.

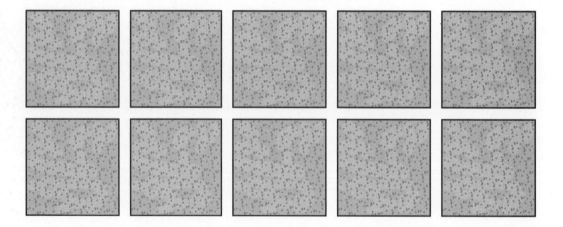

3 Mia works outside with Mrs. Morales. She has 24 square paving tiles to make a garden patio.

Part A   Shade squares on the grid to make a rectangle that is 6 squares long. Then use the rest of the tiles to make more rows. How many rows of 6 did you make with 24 squares?

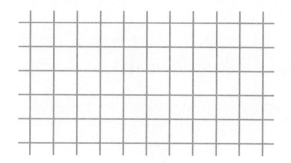

Part B   Shade 24 squares to show a different rectangle. Start with a row of 8 squares. Then use the rest of the tiles to make more rows. How many rows of 8 did you make with 24 squares?

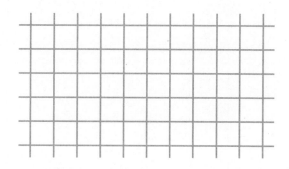

Lesson 37

Domain: Measurement and Data
Cluster: Geometric measurement: understand concepts of area and relate area to multiplication and to addition.
Standards: Primary 3.MD.6; Secondary 3.G.2; Review 2.G.2

Background Information:

Ethan works in a glass factory. He uses square glass panes to make 3 types of windows.

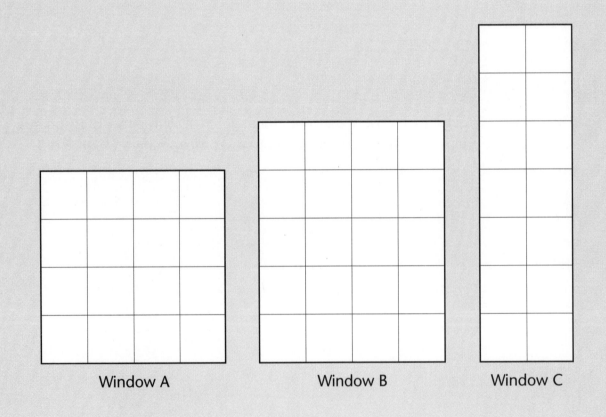

Window A   Window B   Window C

1 Help Ethan choose the window that fills each order.

Part A   One buyer wants a window that has an area of 20 square glass panes.
Should Ethan make Window A, Window B, or Window C for this order?
Explain how you found your answer.

Part B   Another buyer wants a window with an area of 16 square units. Is this
enough information for Ethan to fill the order? Explain why or why not.

2 The picture below shows a different type of window. Ethan says that the area of the window is 8 square units. Dan says it is not 8 square units. Who is correct? Explain the error that the other one makes.

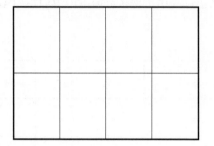

3 Deshawn works in the mirror part of the glass factory. She works with small square mirror tiles.

Part A   Deshawn makes a tiled mirror that is 10 centimeters long. Complete the sentence below. Explain how you found the number and unit of the mirror.

The area of the mirror is _____ square _____.

Part B   Describe Deshawn's mirror that is shown below. What is the total area, the area of dark tiles, and the area of light tiles?

1 cm

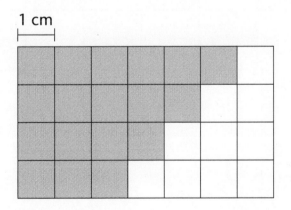

4 Leah makes glass checkerboards. Each glass is a 1-inch square. How many squares does she use? What is the area of the checkerboard?

©RALLY! EDUCATION. No part of this document may be reproduced without written permission from the publisher.

5 Ramón uses glass bricks to make a large window. Each brick is 1 foot wide and 1 foot tall. Using the drawing of the window below, find the area of Ramón's window. How are the number of bricks and the area related?

Lesson 38

Domain: Measurement and Data
Cluster: Geometric measurement: understand concepts of area and relate area to multiplication and to addition.
Standards: Primary 3.MD.7a; Secondary 3.OA.3, 3.G.2; Review 2.G.2

Background Information:

Celia and her friends see many types of electronic screens every day. They find the area of some of them.

1 Celia compares 2 television screens. She draws pictures to compare the screens.

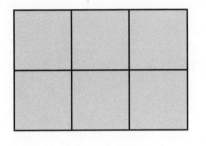

= 1 square foot

Part A   Celia writes some facts about the first screen. Count to find the number to write in each blank. Then explain how Celia could multiply to find the area.

_____ squares across = _____ feet long

_____ rows of squares = _____ feet tall

_____ squares in all = _____ square feet

Part B   Celia shaded 1 square on the second screen. How many squares will fill the screen? What numbers can you multiply to check your answer? What is the area of the screen? Show your work.

2 Celia saw a huge television in a store. It was 6 feet long and 4 feet tall. Complete the drawing below to show the square feet. Write the area of the television. Explain more than one way to find the answer.

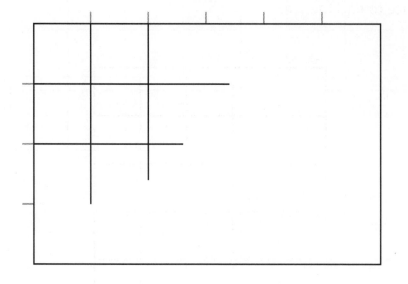

3 Glen likes to read books on his tablet. He places square tiles on top of the tablet to find the area. Each tile is 1 square inch.

Part A   Write numbers on the tiles to count them. Then write a multiplication sentence to find the area.

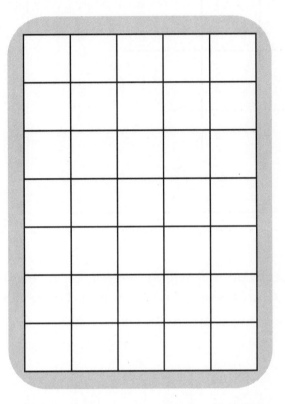

Part B   Look at the numbers that you wrote on the tablet above. What is the area of the tiles numbered 11 to 20? Explain how you solved the problem.

4 Jasmine uses centimeter tiles to cover the screen on her phone. She begins a drawing to show her work. Complete the drawing and find the area of the screen.

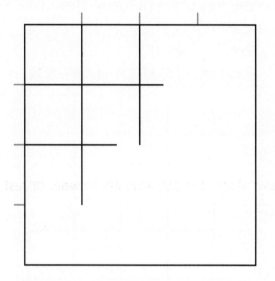

5 Samir compares the screens on two cell phones. He covers each screen with centimeter tiles. Phone A has 6 rows of 4 square tiles. Phone B has 7 rows of 3 square tiles. Make a drawing to show the areas. Which screen is larger? How do you know?

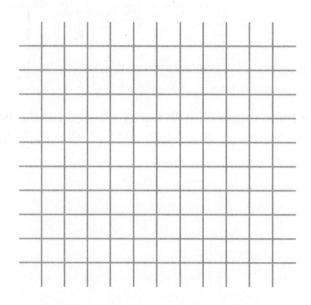

Lesson 39

Domain: Measurement and Data
Cluster: Geometric measurement: understand concepts of area and relate area
to multiplication and to addition.
Standards: Primary 3.MD.7b; Secondary 3.0A.3, 3.NBT.3; Review 2.OA.4

Background Information:

On a farm there are many places for the animals to walk or rest. There are also many places for the animals to eat.

1 Mrs. Sánchez is building stalls in her barn for the animals. The donkeys, horses, and cows will come to the barn to sleep at night. Help Mrs. Sánchez figure out the area of each stall that she needs.

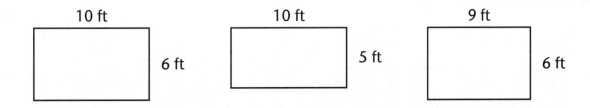

Part A   Mrs. Sánchez builds stalls with the greatest area for the horses. What is the length and width of each horse stall? What is the area? Explain how you solved the problem.

Part B The stalls with the least area will be for the donkeys. What is the size of each donkey stall? What is the area? Show or explain how you found out.

Part C Draw a rectangle on the grid to show the size of each cow stall. Write an addition sentence to find the area of the stall.

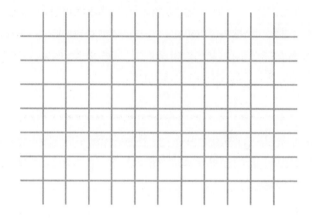

2 Hollis scatters seeds and grain in the yard to feed the chickens. The feeding yard is a 6-foot square. Show more than one way to find the area of the feeding yard.

3 Heather waters the horses in a rectangular trough. The trough is a rectangle that is 14 feet long and 1 foot wide. What is the area of the watering trough? Draw a picture and write a multiplication sentence to show your work.

4 Sabrina is covering part of the barn floor with hay. So far, she has enough hay to cover 24 square feet. In the grid below, each square equals 1 square foot. Draw as many different rectangles as you can to show 24 square feet. Then name a way to show 24 square feet that will not fit on the grid.

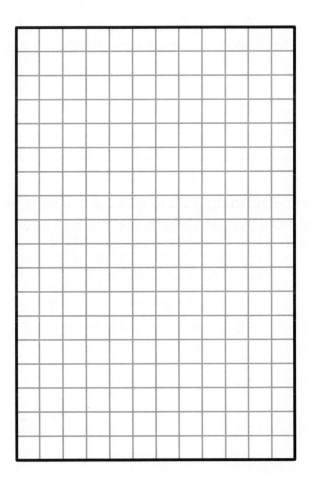

Lesson 40

Domain: Measurement and Data
Cluster: Geometric measurement: understand concepts of area and relate area
to multiplication and to addition.
Standards: Primary 3.MD.7c; Secondary 3.OA.3, 3.NBT.3; Review 2.OA.1

Background Information:

A circus parade may have horses, elephants, and acrobats. They are decorated with horse blankets, drapes, and capes.

1 Marilyn and Cullen sew for the circus. They make two kinds of horse blankets for parades and shows. In the drawings below, each square is 1 square foot.

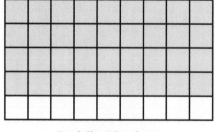

Collar Blankets

Saddle Blankets

Part A   The collar blanket goes over the horse's shoulders. Part of the collar blanket is shaded and part of it is not shaded. The number sentence below can be used to compare the total area of the blanket with the area of both parts of the blanket. Write the numbers that complete the number sentence. What is the total area of the collar blanket? What is the total area of both parts of the blanket?

$$12 \times 3 = \underline{\hspace{1cm}} \times 3 + \underline{\hspace{1cm}} \times 3$$

Part B   Part of the saddle blanket is shaded and part of it is not shaded. The number sentence below can be used to compare the total area of the blanket with area of both parts of the blanket. Write the number that completes the number sentence. What is the total area of the saddle blanket? What is the total area of both parts of the blanket?

$$9 \times 5 = \underline{\hspace{1cm}} (4 + 1)$$

2 Cullen made a different collar blanket for a special show. Shade the blanket to show that $12 \times 4 = 6 \times 4 + 6 \times 4$. What are the areas of each part? Write an addition sentence to show the total area of the blanket.

3 Marilyn made a large drape to cover an elephant's back. The drape is 14 feet long and 8 feet wide. The total area is 112 square feet. What is the combined area of the shaded parts? Show your work. Explain a way to use subtraction to check your answer.

4 The drawing shows a drape for another elephant. The total area is 70 square feet. What is the area of the white part of the drape? Explain why you can use addition, subtraction, or multiplication to solve.

5 The cape for the circus ringmaster is a 5-foot square. He uses the rope at the top to bunch up and tie on the cape. Use the drawing to write the equations for the smaller rectangles. Then show how to add them to find the total area of the cape.

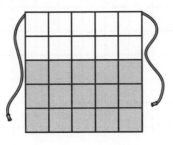

6 Some of the acrobats tie a scarf around their necks for the parade. Each scarf is 9 feet long and 2 feet wide. Draw the scarf on the grid. Shade a square on one end that is 2 feet wide and 2 feet long. Write the area of each part and add to find the total area of the scarf.

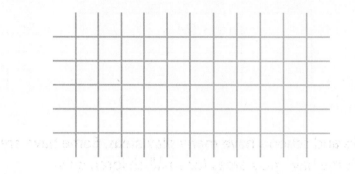

Lesson 41

Domain: Measurement and Data
Cluster: Geometric measurement: understand concepts of area and relate area to multiplication and to addition.
Standards: Primary 3.MD.7d; Secondary 3.OA.3, 3.NBT.3; Review 2.OA.4

Background Information:

Playgrounds in parks and schools have many play areas. Some have areas for swings and slides. Some have play areas for small children only.

1 Mr. Lewis is planning a city park. He needs these sections for the playground. Help Mr. Lewis plan the playground.

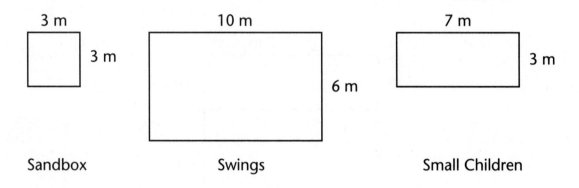

Sandbox   Swings   Small Children

Part A   Find the area of the sandbox and the space for small children. Draw one way to put these spaces together. Then find the area for these two spaces combined. Show your work.

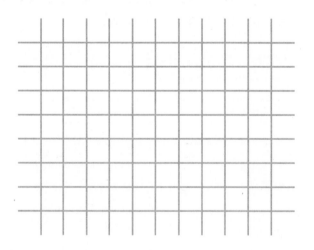

Part B Mr. Lewis draws one way to combine all of the playground spaces. What is the combined area in his drawing? Write the steps that you use to solve the problem.

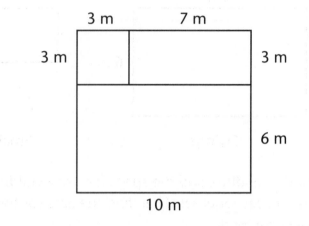

Part C Draw one way to combine the playground spaces that does not make a rectangle. What is the combined area now?

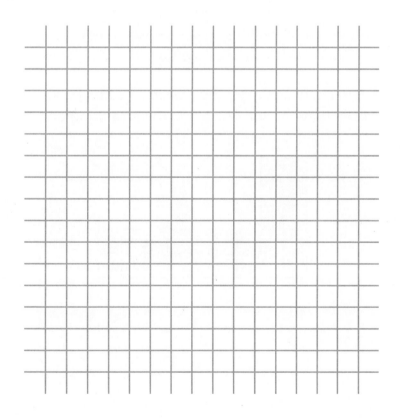

2 One of the sandy areas in Baytown Park is not a rectangle. Use the drawing to find the area. Show your work.

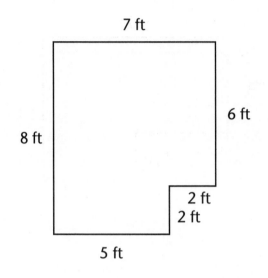

3 Ms. Jones makes a drawing of a playground area in a nearby park. Find the area of the playground. Explain how Ms. Jones can find the area using only addition.

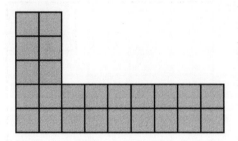

4 There are 2 large slides in one City Park. Use the drawing to find the area that the slides fill. Show your work.

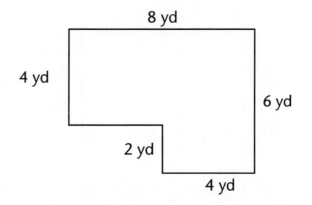

5 The drawing shows a park that has a sandbox in one corner of a playground. Nick says that the combined area of the playground and sandbox is 80 square yards. Dan says that the combined area is 86 square yards. Who is correct? Explain the error that the other person made.

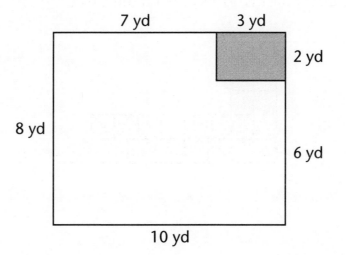

Lesson 42

Domain: Measurement and Data
Cluster: Geometric measurement: understand concepts of area and relate area
to multiplication and to addition.
Standards: Primary 3.MD.7d; Secondary 3.OA.3, 3.NBT.3; Review 2.OA.1

Background Information:

Directors of plays take an empty stage and make it look like a real place. They use tape on the floor to show where to place things. The tape helps the actors know where to stand. This is called blocking a stage.

1 Ms. Herron makes a drawing of her stage to plan the blocking. She makes rectangles and writes the length and width. Help Ms. Herron find the areas of the rectangular blocks.

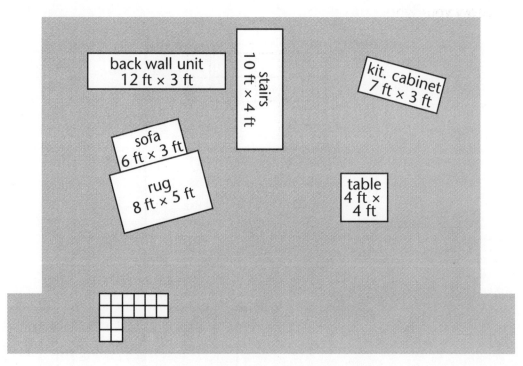

Part A The living room part of the stage has a sofa and a rug. What is the total area that is covered by the sofa and rug? Show your work.

Part B The drawing shows the floor space needed for the back wall unit and the stairs. What is the area of these spaces combined? Show your work.

Part C The part of a stage that is in front of the main curtain is called the apron. It is often used to show an outside scene in front of a house. Look at the apron on Ms. Herron's drawing. It shows a bench that is only on stage part of the play. Each square is 1 square foot. Find the area of the bench. Show your work.

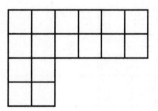

2 The floor space needed for the kitchen table is 4 feet wide and 4 feet long. Ms. Herron wants to add 2 chairs. Use the grid model below to find the total area of the table (shaded) and two chairs (not shaded). Show your work.

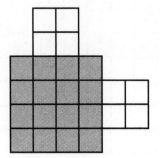

3 Ms. Herron decides to use a different kitchen cabinet on stage. The grid below shows the floor area that the new cabinet covers. Each square is 1 square foot. How many more square feet does it cover than the kitchen cabinet shown on the stage drawing in question 1? Show how to find the area of each cabinet and the difference.

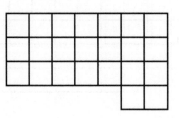

4 Ms. Herron moves the sofa a little bit onto the rug that is on stage. Use the drawing below to find the new area that these pieces cover. Show your work.

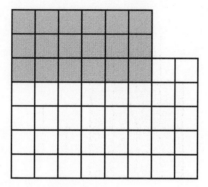

5 Ms. Herron has a small practice stage in her acting class. She draws a model of that stage. Each square is 1 square meter. Use multiplication and addition to find the area of the stage. Show your work.

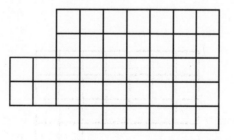

Lesson 43

Domain: Measurement and Data
Cluster: Geometric measurement: recognize perimeter as an attribute of plane figures and distinguish between linear and area measurements.
Standards: Primary 3.MD.8; Secondary 3.OA.3, 3.OA.4; Review 2.OA.1

Background Information:

Ivan sells many types of pools. He measures the spaces where people want to put a pool. Then he helps the people make a choice.

1 Mr. Hovak wants a pool that is a rectangle or square. Ivan shows him some models. Help them find the pools that may work.

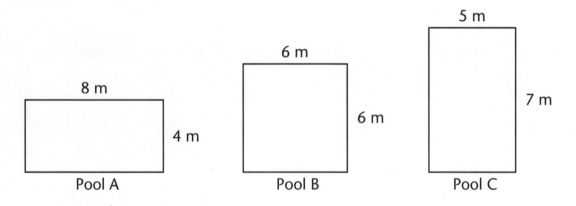

Part A Write all 4 side lengths for each pool. Tell how you found the lengths that are not shown in the models.

Part B   Find and compare the perimeter of each pool. Show your work. Explain how the pools are alike and different.

Part C   Mr. Hovak's pool must fit inside a space that is a 7-meter square. Will each pool fit in his space? Use perimeter and length to explain why or why not.

2 Ms. Sorenson buys a pool that is not a rectangle. The perimeter is 75 feet. Find the length of the side that is not marked. Explain how you found the length.

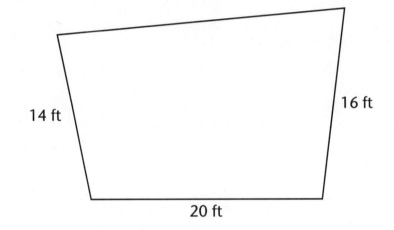

14 ft

16 ft

20 ft

3 Jamal lives in an apartment that has a hot tub beside the pool. The perimeter of the hot tub is 18 feet. Each side is the same length and can be written as a whole number. Which model below shows the shape of the hot tub? Show your work and explain your reasoning.

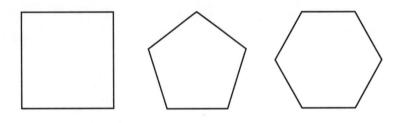

4 Meadows Park has 2 pools. One is a wading pool for young children. Find the perimeter of each pool. Show your work. Are both of the pools rectangles? How do you know?

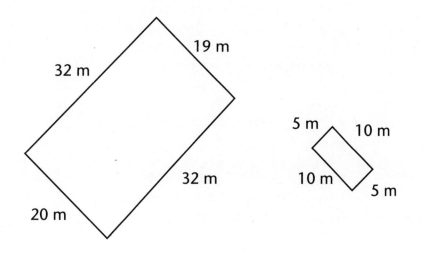

5 The pool models below are rectangles. Which pool has an area that is the same number as its perimeter? Show how you found the perimeter and area of each pool.

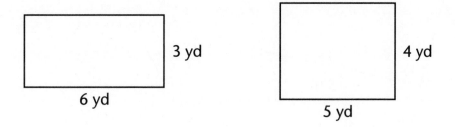

Lesson 44

Domain: Measurement and Data
Cluster: Geometric measurement: recognize perimeter as an attribute of plane figures and distinguish between linear and area measurements.
Standards: Primary 3.MD.8; Secondary 3.OA.3; Review 2.OA.1

Background Information:

Many people like to make gardens. When people plan how to make a garden, they often need to use math to make measurements. Some examples of how math can be used to make a garden are illustrated in this lesson.

 Allison likes to garden. She plants flowers and shrubs in plant beds that are shaped differently. Help Allison plan the amount of trim that she needs for each plant bed.

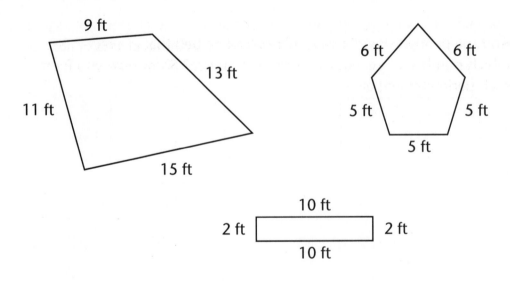

Part A   Allison buys bricks to go around the largest plant bed. Each brick is 1 foot long. How many bricks does she need? Show your work.

Part B   Allison buys bricks to go around the plant bed that has 5 sides. Each brick is 1 foot long. How many bricks does she need? Show your work.

Part C   Find the perimeter and area of Allison's plant bed that is a rectangle. Which number is greater, the perimeter or area? Show how you found each perimeter and area.

2 Mr. Kelso has 2 vegetable gardens in his backyard. Use the rectangle models to compare the gardens. Is the perimeter or the area of the gardens the same? How do you know?

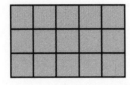

3 Safara draws a model of her rectangular rose garden. She says that the perimeter is 27 feet. Jackie says that the perimeter is 24 feet. Who is correct? What is the mistake that the other girl made?

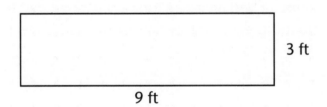

3 ft

9 ft

4 Simon has 24 bricks to frame a plant bed. Draw every possible rectangle that would use all 24 bricks. You do not have to draw a rectangle twice if it is the same rectangle just turned a different way.

Lesson 45

Domain: Measurement and Data
Cluster: Geometric measurement: recognize perimeter as an attribute of plane figures and distinguish between linear and area measurements.
Standards: Primary 3.MD.8; Secondary 3.OA.3; Review 2.OA.1

Background Information:

Gymnastics mats come in many sizes. Some are long and narrow for running or tumbling. Some are huge, thick squares to allow soft landings.

1 Mr. Preston owns a sports store. He makes a table to list all of the gym mats that have an area of 12 square meters.

Part A   Help Mr. Preston complete his table. Write the missing numbers in the table. Then describe any pattern that you see in the table.

Area	Length	Width	Perimeter
12 square meters	1 meter	_____ meters	_____ meters
12 square meters	2 meters	_____ meters	_____ meters
12 square meters	_____ meters	4 meters	_____ meters
12 square meters	_____ meters	3 meters	_____ meters
12 square meters	_____ meters	2 meters	_____ meters
12 square meters	_____ meters	1 meter	_____ meters

Part B   Draw a model of all 6 mats that are shown in Mr. Preston's table.

Part C   Mr. Preston folds the longest mat in half to put it on a shelf. What is the perimeter and area that the mat covers on the shelf?

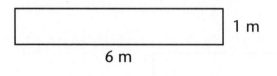

1 m

6 m

2   Yoshi draws a model to prove that her square tumbling mat has the same area and perimeter. Is this true of all squares? Explain why or why not. Draw a model to prove your answer.

3 Cameron draws a tumbling mat that has a perimeter of 20 feet. Draw another mat with the same perimeter but a different area. Write the area of both mats as a number of square feet.

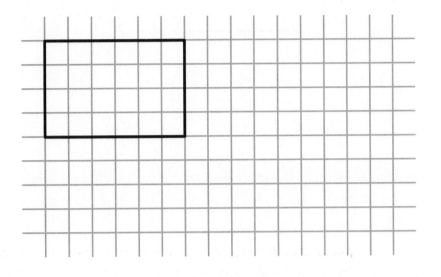

4 Quila has a rectangular exercise mat. The perimeter is 26 feet. The area is 36 square feet. The length of her mat is 9 feet. What is the width? Draw a model of the mat and label all 4 sides.

5 Ian is using a rectangular mat in the gym. The length and width are whole numbers. Ian says that the perimeter is 35 feet. Is this possible? Use an example to explain why or why not.

Chapter 5

Geometry

Chapter 5 focuses on the domain Geometry. The chapter contains lessons. Each lesson covers a cluster and several of the Math Standards in that cluster. For some clusters, there are more than one lesson. The cluster covered in this chapter is listed below.

Cluster:

• Reason with shapes and their attributes.

Lesson 46

Domain: Geometry
Cluster: Reason with shapes and their attributes.
Standards: Primary 3.G.1; Review 2.G.1

Background Information:

Mrs. Diaz's class is studying how to categorize shapes. She reminds the students to look for similarities, such as the number of sides. She then gives her students the following problems to solve. Show how you would solve each problem.

1 What type of shapes do you see below? How are these shapes the same?

2 Part A   Draw a quadrilateral. Draw a rhombus. How are the shapes you drew alike? How are they different?

Part B   Is a quadrilateral always a rhombus? Is a rhombus always a quadrilateral? Explain.

3 Part A Draw a square, a rectangle, and a rhombus. Explain why a square can also be named a rectangle or a rhombus.

Part B Explain why a rectangle cannot be named a rhombus.

4 Look at the quadrilaterals shown below.

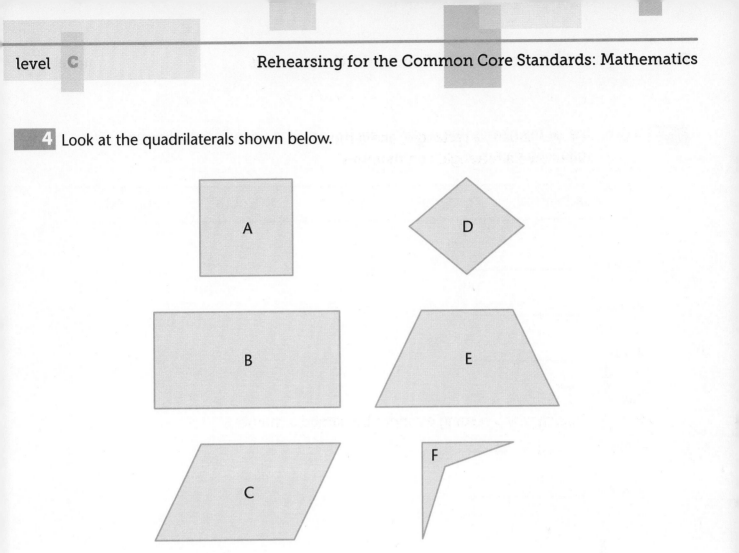

Part A   List the quadrilaterals that appear to have—

• 4 right angles:

• 2 pairs of opposite sides that are parallel:

• No right angles:

Part B List all the names that describe each shape shown in Part A. Use the following names.

quadrilateral	rectangle	square	rhombus	trapezoid

Shape A: _____

Shape B: _____

Shape C: _____

Shape D: _____

Shape E: _____

Shape F: _____

Lesson 47

Domain: Geometry
Cluster: Reason with shapes and their attributes.
Standards: Primary 3.G.1; Review 2.G.1

Background Information:

Geometric shapes are all around us. Many pieces of art contain geometric shapes. Emma's art class is studying geometric shapes found in art. This week, the class is focusing on quadrilaterals. Her teacher displayed this piece of art that is made up of various quadrilaterals.

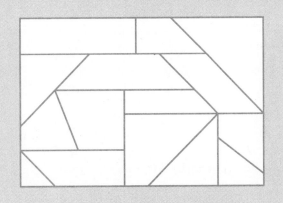

1 Emma's teacher wrote the following assignment on the board. Show how Emma can complete the assignment.

I am a polygon with 4 sides and 4 angles. At least one of my angles is less than a right angle. Draw what I look like. List all of the shapes that name what I am. Explain why these different names can be used for the same polygon.

2 Emma glued together craft sticks to form this shape.

Part A   Name the shape Emma made. How do you know?

Part B   Describe how Emma could rearrange the craft sticks to form a square.

3 The art teacher gave each student a piece of grid paper. She asked the students to draw an example of a quadrilateral that is not a square, a rectangle, a trapezoid, or a rhombus.

Part A   On the grid paper below, draw a quadrilateral that matches the description given in the assignment.

Part B   Explain why the shape you drew in Part A can be classified as a quadrilateral but cannot be classified as a square, a rectangle, a trapezoid, or a rhombus.

4 The art teacher gave Emma 4 straws of equal length.

Part A   Name the quadrilaterals that Emma can make with the 4 straws. Explain.

Part B   The art teacher asks Emma to cut 1 straw in half. Emma uses the 2 halves and 2 of the other straws to make a quadrilateral. Name the quadrilateral Emma can make. Explain.

Lesson 48

Domain: Geometry
Cluster: Reason with shapes and their attributes.
Standards: Primary 3.G.2; Secondary 3.NF.1, 3.MD.6; Review 2.G.3

Background Information:

Gardeners often divide a garden plot into equal parts. They can then place different kinds of plants in each area.

1 Sari is making a flower garden in the shape of a hexagon. She will divide the garden into equal-sized parts and plant different colored flowers in each part of the garden.

Part A   Sari wants to divide her garden into 2 equal parts. Draw a line down the middle of the hexagon below to divide it into 2 parts that have an equal area. What new shapes are formed? What fraction names each part of the whole you divided?

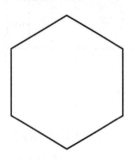

Part B   Explain why the two shapes in Part A have the same area.

Part C   Sari has decided that she would like to include more colors in her garden, so she will divide the hexagon into 4 equal parts. Show how Sari can divide the hexagon into 4 shapes that have equal areas. Then, write the fraction that names each part.

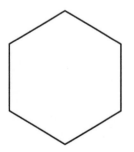

2 Jamie is making a vegetable garden. His garden is shaped like a rectangle. He divides the rectangle into 4 parts that have an equal area as shown below. He will plant a different vegetable in each part of the garden.

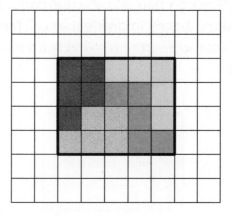

Part A   What fraction names each part of the divided whole? What do you notice about the shapes you see after the garden is divided?

Part B   Is the area of each part of the garden the same? Explain.

3 Nicole is also making a vegetable garden. Her garden is shaped like a rectangle. She wants to divide the rectangle into 6 parts that have an equal area. She will plant a different vegetable in each part of the garden.

Part A   Draw lines to divide the rectangle below into 6 parts that have an equal area. Were you able to draw all parts with the same shape? Explain. What fraction names each part of the divided whole?

Part B   Is the area of each part of the garden the same? Explain.

Lesson 49

Domain: Geometry
Cluster: Reason with shapes and their attributes.
Standards: Primary 3.G.2; Secondary 3.NF.1; Review 2.G.3

Background Information:

Gil's Glass Shop makes custom windows. All of the windows begin as a basic geometric shape. The window shapes are then divided into equal parts. Each part is outlined with wood or metal strips to help support and protect the glass.

1 One customer wants a window that is shaped like a trapezoid and can be divided into 3 equal parts. Draw lines to divide the trapezoid below into 3 parts that have an equal area. What new shapes are formed? What fraction names the area of each part of the whole window?

2 Gil's Glass Shop has been called out to install a window on a house. The opening for the window is shown by the shaded area in the picture below. Gil thinks the window will need to be divided into 4 equal parts. Draw lines to divide the shape into 4 equal parts. What fraction is each part of the whole window? What is the area of each part?

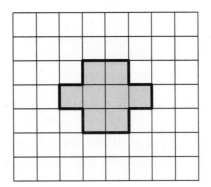

3 Another customer has a window shaped like a rhombus. Draw a line to divide the shape into 2 equal parts. What fraction is each part of the whole window?

4 Gil's Glass Shop has 2 customers who want square windows. Both square windows are equal in size. One customer wants the window divided into equal halves like this.

The other customer wants the window divided into equal halves like this.

Are the halves of one window greater in area that the halves of the other window? Explain.

219

5 Gil has a stack of pieces of glass that are shaped like triangles. He can use the triangular pieces of glass to make windows with other shapes.

Part A   How many triangles are in 1 rhombus? What fraction best describes each triangle in the rhombus?

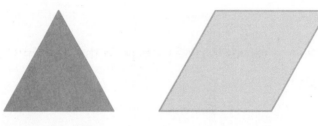

How many triangles are in 1 trapezoid? What fraction best describes each triangle in the trapezoid?

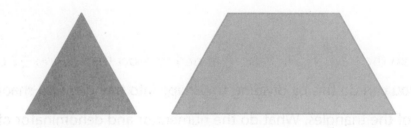

How many triangles are in 1 hexagon? What fraction best describes each triangle in the hexagon?

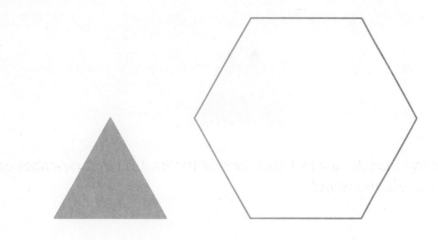

Part B   Does the fraction $\frac{1}{3}$ represent the triangle in the rhombus and in the hexagon? Explain.

Part C   How can the trapezoid in Part A be used to show the fraction $\frac{2}{3}$? Explain how you can do this by dividing the shape into triangles and shading some of the triangles. What do the numerator and denominator of the fraction $\frac{2}{3}$ represent?

Chapter 6

Review

Chapter 6 is a review and reinforcement chapter. The math problems in this chapter cover various domains, clusters, and standards. This chapter is divided into lessons, and each problem in a lesson may cover different domains.

Lesson 50

Standards: 3.OA.1, 3.OA.5, 3.NBT.1, 3.NF.1, 3.NF.3d, 3.OA.3, 3.OA.7, 3.NBT.3, 3.G.2; Review 2.G.3

1 Ryan has 7 toy cars in a box. He wants to know the total number of wheels on all the cars in the box.

Part A How many wheels does each car have? How many equal groups of wheels are there? Draw a model to show the number of groups of wheels and the number of wheels in each group.

Part B Explain how you can use the model you drew in Part A to find the total number of wheels on all the cars in the box. How many wheels in all are on the cars?

2 Sophia has the following problem as part of her homework.

$$9 \times 3 = \underline{\hspace{1cm}}$$

She was told to use the Distributive Property to find the product. Show how to use the Distributive Property by using addends for one of the factors. Find the product.

3 Jennifer has 40 yellow beads in her craft box. She has twice as many red beads and 3 times as many blue beads. Rounded to the nearest 100, about how many beads does Jennifer have in all?

4 In Prove It, players take turns drawing a card. Each card has a math statement that may or may not be true. Players must prove that the statement is true or false. They can draw a picture or show their work another way.

Part A Kristie gets to choose the first card.

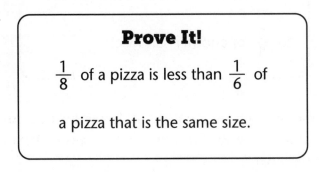

> ### Prove It!
>
> $\frac{1}{8}$ of a pizza is less than $\frac{1}{6}$ of
>
> a pizza that is the same size.

Kristie says that the statement is true. Beth argues that it is false because 8 is greater than 6. Part of Kristie's picture is below. Complete Kristie's picture. Is the card true or false?

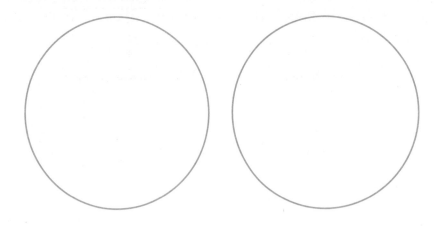

Part B   Tim chooses the next card.

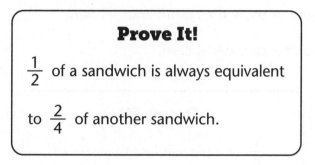

> ### Prove It!
>
> $\frac{1}{2}$ of a sandwich is always equivalent
>
> to $\frac{2}{4}$ of another sandwich.

Tim draws a picture to prove that the statement is true. Rico thinks of a way to prove that it is false. Tim's drawing is below. Draw a picture that Rico may have drawn.

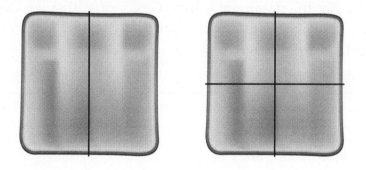

Part C   Do you think that Tim or Rico gets the point for the Prove It card? Explain why you think so.

Lesson 51

Standards: 3.OA.6, 3.MD.1, 3.MD.5b, 3.MD.7b, 3.MD.8, 3.G.1, 3.OA.7, 3.MD.7a;
Review 2.OA.1, 2.G.1

1 Ryan and his friends go to a camp for 1 week. There are many boys and girls there. When they check in, they get a schedule of activities for the first day.

Day 1 at Camp Clearlake

Activity	Time
Check in and put up tents	8:30 to 11:30
Lunch in dining hall	11:30 to 12:30
Swimming lessons or free time	1:00 to 2:25
Canoe lessons or free time	2:00 to 3:25
Arts and crafts classes or free time	3:00 to 4:25

How much longer than 1 hour does each group lesson or class last? Is it possible for Ryan and his friends to go to all 3 afternoon activities? Can they go to 2 classes? Explain why or why not.

2 Liz makes a chart to show the length and width of her favorite pictures.

Picture	Length	Width
Mom catching a fish	8 inches	5 inches
Stephen cooking breakfast	10 inches	9 inches
Aunt Margaret in a canoe	4 inches	3 inches
Liz climbing a tree	5 inches	7 inches
Katy hugging Grandpa	3 inches	4 inches

Part A   Which 2 pictures have the same area? Do they also have the same perimeter? Explain why or why not.

Part B   Liz uses 1-inch square tiles to find the area of each picture. Look at the tiles in the models. Write Mom or Liz under the model that is the size of their picture. Then, write the area for each picture. Show your work.

Part C   What is the perimeter of the picture that shows Liz climbing a tree? Show your work.

3   Alina made 36 biscuits and 30 corn muffins for a neighborhood picnic. She put the biscuits and corn muffins in baskets. Each basket could hold either 6 biscuits or 6 corn muffins. How many baskets did Alina use in all for the biscuits and corn muffins? Show your work.

4 Part A Draw a quadrilateral. Draw a rectangle. How are the shapes you drew alike? How are they different?

Part B Is a quadrilateral always a rectangle? Is a rectangle always a quadrilateral? Explain.

Lesson 52

Standards: 3.OA.2, 3.OA.7, 3.NBT.1, 3.NF.3b, 3.MD.3, 3.MD.8, 3.OA.3, 3.OA.8;
Review 2.OA.1, 2.OA.3

1 Alden has a card that shows a rectangle divided into equal thirds. His card is shown below. Draw a model that shows a fraction that is equivalent to the fraction shown by the rectangle.

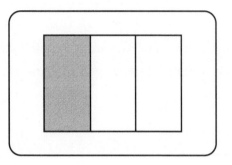

2 Emily has 12 sea shells that she wants to place in equal groups. Show 2 different ways Emily can make equal groups of sea shells.

3 At the deli, Andy buys 3 pounds of turkey and 2 pounds of cheese. The turkey costs $7 per pound and the cheese costs $6 per pound. What is the total amount Andy pays for the turkey and cheese? Show your work.

4 There are an odd number of houses in Nathan's neighborhood. Rounded to the nearest hundred, the number of homes is 200. Find the least number and the greatest number of homes that could be in Nathan's neighborhood.

5 Liz makes a frame to put around a 9-inch by 10-inch picture. She uses 4 straight twigs that she found to make the frame. What is the length of each twig? What is the perimeter of the picture?

6 The picture graph shows the number of campers who chose each activity on the first day of camp.

Campers in Each Activity on Day 1

Activity	Number of Campers
Swimming	👤 👤 👤 👤 👤 👤
Canoeing	👤 👤 👤 👤
Arts and Crafts	👤 👤 👤
Hiking	👤 👤 👤 👤 👤

👤 = 5 campers

Part A   How many campers chose a water activity? Explain the steps you used to solve the problem.

Part B   How many more campers chose hiking than arts and crafts? Show your work.

Lesson 53

Standards: 3.OA.2, 3.OA.7, 3.NBT.2, 3.NF.3c, 3.MD.3, 3.G.1, 3.OA.3, 3.OA.6, 3.OA.8; Review 2.OA.1

1 Clarissa has a card that shows a circle with $\frac{2}{2}$ shaded. Draw a different circle model that shows a fraction that is equivalent to the fraction shown on Clarissa's card.

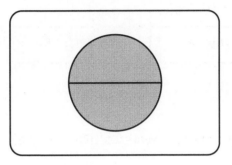

2 Ryan has 15 blue toy cars. He wants to place the cars in 3 rows with an equal number of cars in each row. How many cars should Ryan put in each row? Show your work.

3 Antonio had 28 songs on his MP3 player. He created 5 playlists and put an equal number of songs in each playlist. He had 3 songs left that he did not put in a playlist. How many songs did Antonio put in each playlist? Show your work.

4 A local gym started the month with 312 members. During the month, 85 people joined the gym and 37 people cancelled their membership. How many members did the gym have at the end of the month? Show your work.

5 Amanda drew the following shape on a piece of paper. Explain why Amanda's shape can be classified as a quadrilateral but cannot be classified as a square, a rectangle, a trapezoid, or a rhombus.

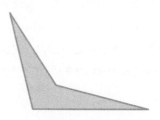

6 The bar graph shows the activities that girls chose on the second day at Camp Clearlake.

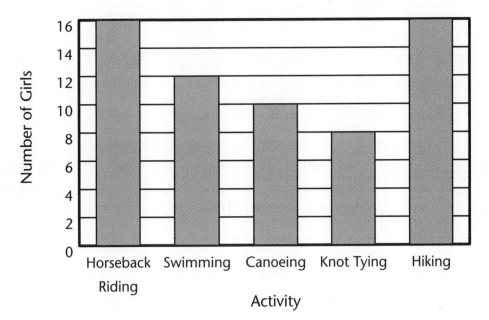

Girls' Choices for Day 2 Activities

Part A   Which 2 activities tied for the most popular choice? How many girls altogether chose those activities? Show your work.

Part B   Did more girls choose the 2 most popular activities or the other 3 activities combined? Show your work and use < or > to write a comparison.

Lesson 54

Standards: 3.OA.3, 3.OA.8, 3.NBT.2, 3.NF.3c, 3.MD.7b, 3.G.1, 3.OA.2, 3.MD.8; Review 2.G.1

1 Stephen took a picture of his sister in a tree. She is making a funny face. Stephen prints the picture. It is 10 inches long and 8 inches wide. Draw a rectangle on the grid to model the picture. Find the area and perimeter.

2 Ryan has 24 toy cars that he wants to give to 4 of his friends. He wants to give an equal number of toy cars to each friend. He decides to place the toy cars in an array. Describe how Ryan can use an array to divide the toy cars evenly. How many toy cars will he give to each friend?

3 Hailey is setting up chairs for a meeting. There are 32 chairs in all. Hailey is able to place an equal number of chairs in 4 rows. There are 4 chairs left over. How many chairs did Hailey put in each row? Show your work.

4 Mr. Davis had some money. He spent $34 on groceries and $21 to buy a shirt. He has $110 left. How much money did Mr. Davis have before he bought groceries and a shirt? Show your work.

5 Clarissa finds a card that she thinks is a match for $\frac{2}{2}$, but she is not sure. Is it a match? Explain why or why not.

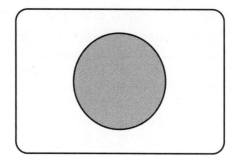

6 Aunt Margaret bought some postcards on vacation. Find the area and perimeter of the postcard model below. Then, draw another rectangle that has the same area but a different perimeter.

7 Read the description of a shape given below. List all the shape names that could apply to the shape. Explain.

> I am a polygon with 4 sides and 4 angles.
> At least one of my angles is greater than a right angle.

Lesson 55

Standards: 3.OA.3, 3.OA.8, 3.NBT.2, 3.NF.2a, 3.MD.4, 3.G.2, 3.OA.2, 3.NF.1, 3.NF.3a; Review 2.OA.1

1 Some campers entered a potato-tossing contest on the last day of camp. In round 1 of the contest, the top five distances were rounded to the nearest half of a foot. The table shows the distances and the number of campers who made them.

Potato Tossing

Distance in Feet	Number of Campers
22	2
$22\frac{1}{2}$	1
23	3
$23\frac{1}{2}$	2
24	4

Part A   Use the data in the chart to complete the line plot.

Potato Tossing

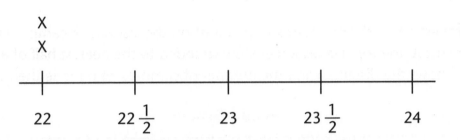

Part B   How many campers tossed a potato 23 feet or more? Explain how the line
plot makes it easy to find or check your answer.

2 Emily had 17 books. She gave 3 books to a friend. She put the remaining books in 2 boxes. She put the same number of books in each box. How many books did Emily put in each box? Show your work.

3 Jeff has to mail 4 small boxes and 3 large boxes. It costs $3 to send each small box and $6 to send each large box. How much money does Jeff need in all to mail the boxes? Show your work.

4 Abby and Taylor kept track of the number of pages they read over the summer. Abby read 314 pages. The number of pages Taylor read is 44 less than double the number of pages Abby read. How many pages did Taylor read? Show your work.

5 Brad and Sophie each have a card. Part of the rectangle on each card is shaded. Each card represents a fraction. They draw number lines to compare the fractions. Mark the point for each fraction on the number lines. Do their cards show equivalent fractions? Explain how you know.

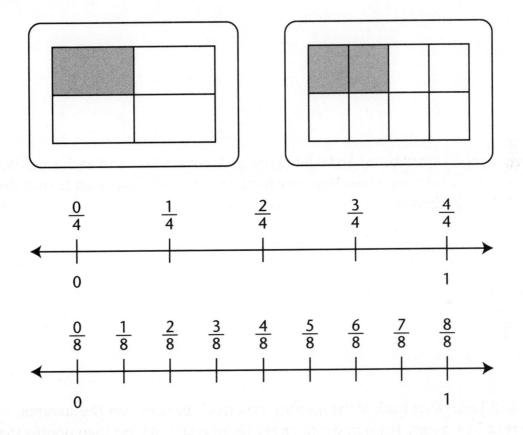

6 Keith has a piece of tile shaped like a rhombus. He wants to divide the tile into two equal parts. Draw a line to divide the tile into two parts with equal area. What new shapes are formed? What fraction names each part of the whole you divided?

Lesson 56

Standards: 3.OA.4, 3.OA.9, 3.NBT.3, 3.MD.8, 3.G.2, 3.OA.2, 3.OA.3, 3.NF.1, 3.MD.6;
Review 2.OA.1

Background Information:

Julia is making a flower garden. Her garden is shaped like a rectangle. She divides the rectangle into 3 parts with equal areas as shown below. She will plant a different kind of flower in each part of the garden. Use the diagram to answer questions 1 and 2.

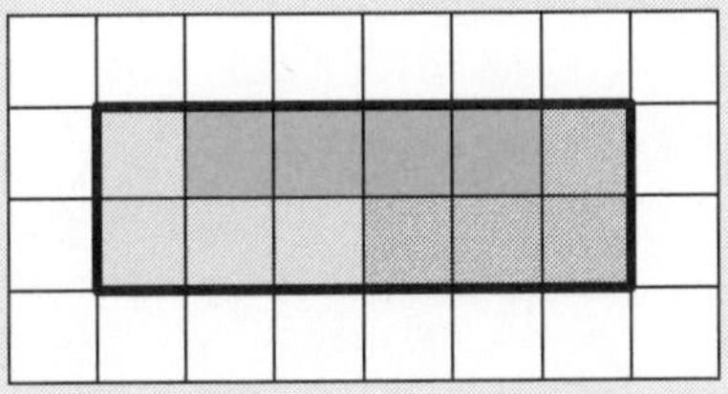

What unit fraction names each part of the garden after it is divided?

2 What do you notice about the shapes of the different parts of the garden? Is the area of each part of the garden the same? Explain.

3 Emily wants to display 18 trophies on shelves. She places an equal number of trophies on 3 shelves. This equation represents the situation.

$$18 \div d = 3$$

What strategy can you use to find the unknown number? What is the unknown number? What does this number represent?

4 Liz drew a picture to send to Grandpa. She used a piece of paper that is not a rectangle. The perimeter of the picture is 43 inches. What is the length of the side that is not labeled? Show your work.

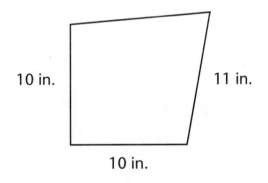

10 in.   11 in.

10 in.

5 Mrs. Mayfield is ordering bookmarks with the school logo on them for a fundraiser. She has 2 boxes of bookmarks in her office. There are 5 bundles of bookmarks in each box of bookmarks. Each bundle of bookmarks has 50 bookmarks. Mrs. Mayfield wants to have 750 bookmarks available for the fundraiser. How many more bookmarks should she order? Show your work.

6 Nelson wants to earn $160 by walking dogs. He earns $20 a week, and he has worked 4 weeks so far. How much more does Nelson need to earn to reach his goal? Show your work.

7 Complete the columns for 1, 5, and 6 in the multiplication table.

×	1	2	3	4	5	6	7	8	9	10
1										
2										
3										
4										
5										
6										
7										
8										
9										
10										

Look across each row and compare the products. What do you notice?